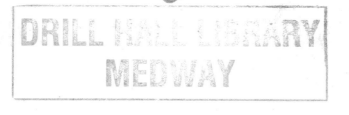

ConstructionSkills
Managerial and Professional
Health & Safety Test

All the Questions and Answers
for tests taken from August 2009

constructionskills

Published by ConstructionSkills
Bircham Newton, King's Lynn
Norfolk PE31 6RH

© Construction Industry Training Board 2009

The Construction Industry Training Board otherwise known as
CITB-ConstructionSkills and ConstructionSkills is a registered charity
(Charity Number: 264289)

First Published 2006
Revised 2007
Revised with new title 2009

ISBN: 978-1-85751-999-0

Produced by Prometric
Printed in the UK

Contents

Introduction

For the last six years, industry bodies and construction employers have rated health and safety as a top priority. Even in these difficult times, the health and safety of our workforce is crucial and it is essential that we do not compromise on standards.

Around half a million people take the Health & Safety Test every year and over time we have made a number of important changes, including introducing mobile testing vehicles to widen testing capacity so that we can respond to the industry's need for site-based skills assessment.

More recently, we introduced the SkillsDirect service, which ties health and safety more closely to the process of getting qualified and carded – taking us a step closer to our vision of achieving a fully qualified workforce.

The introduction of the ConstructionSkills Managerial and Professional Health and Safety Test is a significant marker extending the scope of the Test to the non-site based professionals who contribute so much to the industry and who have a significant impact on health and safety on site.

We are delighted to have received so much support from this sector and that so many key industry bodies have become involved in setting the standards for the Test to ensure it meets the needs of the sector and of our industry. We thank them for this input, and look forward to their continued support.

On that point, I'm very pleased that Keith Clarke, CEO of Atkins, has agreed to write the foreword for this question book to add his view on the significance of the test to this sector of industry.

Sir Michael Latham
Chairman
ConstructionSkills

Foreword

The expectation that the construction industry is inherently dangerous is finally changing due to the efforts of all parts of the industry. It is vital we provide a safe and dignified working environment that all involved can feel proud of.

The role of off-site professionals in raising the health and safety agenda – whether they are architects, engineers, quantity surveyors or the many other disciplines involved in the design and procurement process – is significant and, until recently, underestimated. The introduction of the ConstructionSkills for Managerial and Professional Health and Safety Test will now address this gap, and should have enormous influence, not just on the construction techniques used, but also on the values and ethos of the sites themselves.

Safety is not about policing but about behaviour and the broad and deep consensus that unsafe sites or activities are simply unacceptable in any circumstances. This is the responsibility of us all.

Getting a CSCS or affiliated card is a strong sign that a fully trained workforce is key and that we all, as professionals, need to show leadership by example and not be escorted visitors on our own sites.

We have a great industry – it must become a healthy and safe one for all those working in it.

Keith Clarke
Chief Executive
Atkins Group

Preparing for the Health and Safety Test

For many years the construction industry has had more than its fair share of serious accidents and deaths. Lack of training and little awareness of danger have been factors that have contributed to this unacceptable accident record with many accidents occurring because the same mistakes are repeated over and over again. The ConstructionSkills Health and Safety Test helps raise standards across the industry by ensuring that workers meet a minimum level of health and safety awareness before going on site. It now forms a key part of most major card schemes, including CSCS and its affiliates.

The test has been running for over eight years and underwent significant improvements including an enhanced delivery infrastructure in April 2005*. The addition of the Managerial and Professional Test ensures the test continues to meet the needs of our industry.

This guide has been written to help you prepare for the Managerial and Professional Health and Safety Test.

Each test will comprise 50 questions. You will be allowed 45 minutes for the test.

* Health and Safety Test questions and answers do change from time to time in line with regulations. ConstructionSkills will make every effort to keep the test book up-to-date. ConstructionSkills will not test any candidates on any questions that are no longer in line with legislation and will not test any candidates on any questions that do not feature in the most up-to-date published book.

Preparing for the Health and Safety Test

You should read through this guide and attempt some of the questions from each section before attending the test. This will give you an idea of your strengths and weaknesses, and indicate the areas where you may need to improve your knowledge.

You can also attend one of the courses run by our National Construction College – call us on 0344 994 4433 to find out more.

The purpose of the test is to help reinforce the existing health and safety knowledge of professionally qualified persons who, although engaged in the project, are not based on site. Legislation and professional Codes of Conduct place obligations upon professionally qualified people to assess a situation and respond in an appropriate way. The Managerial and Professional Health and Safety Test helps provide information on common site hazards and how the professional person may be expected to react.

The self-employed

Many of the questions will refer to the duties of employers. In law, the self-employed have the same legal responsibilities as employers. To keep the questions as brief as possible, the wording only refers to the duties of employers, and not to the duties of the self-employed, but the questions apply to both.

Your level of knowledge

In sitting the Managerial and Professional Test it will be expected that you have a working knowledge of the CDM Regulations. It is also expected that you will have prepared yourself for the Health and Safety Test by using the revision material contained in this book.

Northern Ireland legislation

All questions in this book are based on British legislation. However, Northern Ireland legislation may differ from that in the rest of the UK.

For practical reasons, all candidates (including those in Northern Ireland) will be tested on questions using legislation relevant to the rest of the UK only.

Booking your Health and Safety Test

The easiest ways to book your test are online or by telephone. You will be given the date and time of your test immediately. The test can also be booked by postal/fax application. You should expect that tests will be available 3 to 8 weeks from when you book.

The test is offered in over 150 Prometric test centres throughout the UK. The list of centres is available online at **www.cskills.org/hstest**

What you need to be able to make a booking

To make a test booking you will need
1. Your ConstructionSkills registration number – new applicants will be able to register by calling **0344 994 4488**.
   If you have previously booked a test with us or are a member of CSCS, you will be asked to provide your individual ID number.
2. To know which category of test you need to take.
3. A method of payment – credit or debit card for online, telephone, post or fax bookings, or a cheque or postal order if sending your application.

Online

You can make, check or change a test booking 24 hours a day, 7 days a week at **www.cskills.org/hstest**

You will receive an email confirming your test booking along with directions to the test centre. It is important that you check the details in this confirmation and follow any instructions it gives regarding the test.

Telephone

To book your test by telephone, call:

0344 994 4488

The registration centre is open between 8am and 6pm, Monday to Friday. All the details of your test will be confirmed with you during the call and again in a letter that you should receive within 10 days. It is important that you check the details in this confirmation and follow any instructions it gives regarding the test.

Booking your Health and Safety Test

By post/fax

If you prefer to book by post or fax you need to use the application form available at **www.cskills.org/hstest** or by calling **0344 994 4488**. If you are making a booking for a group of candidates please ask for the Group Booking application form.

Special needs

If you have any special requirements for taking the test, such as reading difficulties or preferring to take the test in a language other than English, please advise us at the time of booking.

Corporate Mobile Testing

For organisations wishing to test a group of candidates at their place of work, please call 0161 868 9255 for details of the corporate mobile testing service.

What if I don't receive a confirmation letter?

If you do not receive a confirmation letter within the time specified, please telephone 0344 994 4488 to check that your test booking has been made.

We cannot take responsibility for postal delays. If you miss your test event, you will unfortunately forfeit your fee.

How do I cancel or postpone my test?

To cancel or postpone your test you should go online or call the booking number at least three clear working days before your test date, otherwise you'll lose your fee.

Only in exceptional circumstances, such as documented ill health or family bereavement, can this rule be waived.

Please note that any reschedules made via our telephone booking line 0344 994 4488 will incur a £5 reschedule fee. There will be no charge for rescheduling online outside of the 3 working day penalty period.

Duplicate Result Letters

It is important that the result letter you are given on completing the Test is kept safe as any requests for results or duplicate pass certificates must be sent in writing to
CARES Customer Service Team, Prometric, Exchange Quay, Salford Quays, Manchester, M5 3EA and these requests will incur a £10 admin charge.

Taking your Health and Safety Test

Please allow plenty of time to get to the test centre as you may not be able to take the test if you arrive after your session has started. You should also ensure that you bring all relevant documentation with you or you will not be able to sit your test and you will lose your fee.

You will need:
- your confirmation email or letter
- ID bearing your photo and signature (e.g. driving licence or passport)
- any other items listed on your confirmation letter.

When you arrive at the test centre please follow the ConstructionSkills or Prometric branded signs. Upon arrival, the test centre staff will check your documents and ensure you are booked onto the correct category of test.

During the test

The tests are all delivered on a computer screen. However you do not need to be familiar with computers, and the test does not involve any writing. All you will need to do is select the relevant answer boxes, using either a mouse or by touching the screen.

Before the test begins you can sit a practice session to get used to the way the test will work.

The test will contain a number of multiple-choice questions. Most questions will give four answers, only one of which is correct. You must select the answer that you think is correct. Some questions will require you to select two correct answers from four or five, and others require three correct from a choice of five. Each question will be clearly marked with the number of correct answers that you must find.

You will be allowed 45 minutes for the test.

At the end of the test there is an optional survey which gives you the chance to provide feedback on the test process.

If you fail the test you will receive feedback on the section in which you got questions wrong before leaving the test centre. If you do not reach the required standard you are strongly advised to read again all of the topic areas appropriate to your test. If you fail the test, you'll have to wait at least three clear working days before you take the test again.

It is becoming increasingly important to carry the right card to prove your skills on construction sites.

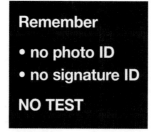

Remember

- **no photo ID**
- **no signature ID**

NO TEST

Once you have passed your Health and Safety Test, you should apply to join the appropriate card scheme for your trade. In most cases, this will be CSCS (Construction Skills Certification Scheme) or an affiliated scheme.

Your pass letter should include contact details of all relevant schemes you can apply to.

You can find out more about many of the schemes at **www.cskills.org/cardschemes**

Scheme contact details

To contact CSCS, which covers most schemes in the industry, telephone **0844 576 8777** or go to **www.cscs.uk.com**

To contact CPCS, which covers the operation of construction plant machinery, telephone **0844 815 7274** or go to **www.cskills.org/cpcs**

10

All candidates will be asked questions from the Core test sections, which include:

- Section 1   General Responsibilities
- Section 2   Accident Prevention and Reporting
- Section 3   Health and Welfare
- Section 4   Manual Handling
- Section 5   Working at Height
- Section 6   Personal Protective Equipment (PPE)
- Section 7   Emergency Procedures and First Aid
- Section 8   Safe Use of Hazardous Substances
- Section 9   Electrical Safety and Hand Tools
- Section 10   Fire Prevention and Control
- Section 11   Safety Signs and Signals
- Section 12   Site Transport, Plant and Lifting Operations
- Section 13   Noise and Vibration
- Section 14   Excavations and Confined Spaces
- Section 15   Supervisory and Management
- Section 16   Demolition
- Section 17   Plumbing or Gas
- Section 18   Highway Works

General Responsibilities

1.1

During site induction, you do not understand something the presenter says. What should you do?

☐ A: Attend another site induction

☐ B: Ask the presenter to explain the point again

☐ C: Guess what the presenter was trying to tell you

☐ D: Wait until the end then ask someone else to explain

1.2

A Permit to Work allows:

☐ A: the emergency services to come on to the site after an accident

☐ B: certain jobs to be carried out under controlled conditions

☐ C: HSE inspectors to visit the site

☐ D: untrained people to work without supervision

1.3

Now that work on site has moved forward, the safety rules given in your site induction seem out of date. What should you do?

☐ A: Do nothing, you are not responsible for safety on site

☐ B: Speak to the site manager about your concerns

☐ C: Speak to your colleagues to see if they have any new rules

☐ D: Decide yourself what to do to suit the changing conditions

1.4

You are aware that a Prohibition Notice has been placed on some site equipment. What does this mean?

☐ A: It must not be used unless the operatives are supervised

☐ B: It must not be used until serious safety issues have been rectified

☐ C: It can only be used under the supervision of an HSE inspector

☐ D: Only supervisors can use it

1.5

If you discover children playing on site, what is the **first** priority?

☐ A: Tell the site manager

☐ B: Phone the police

☐ C: Ensure the safety of the children

☐ D: Find out how they got into the site

Answers: 1.1 = B, 1.2 = B, 1.3 = B, 1.4 = B, 1.5 = C

1.6

If you see environmental incidents and near misses while on site, when should you report these?

A: Never, this is a problem for the contractor

B: During your next break

C: As soon as practical

D: At the end of the day just before you leave site

1.7

Where would you expect to see rubbish or other leftover materials put at the end of a work activity?

A: Left where it is

B: Picked up and thrown with rubbish left by other people

C: Put in a designated waste area

D: Picked up and dumped outside the site

1.8

Before you are allowed to start work for the first time on a new site you should:

A: sign in at security

B: be shown where the toilets and drinking water are

C: be given safety wellingtons

D: receive induction training

1.9

Checking your identity and the purpose of your visit before allowing you on site:

A: is part of the contractor's systems to ensure that the site is properly monitored and controlled

B: is a waste of time and petty bureaucracy

C: enables the client to check up on you to see if you earned your fee

D: is an example of security measures being too strict

1.10

Who is responsible for reporting any unsafe conditions on site?

A: The site manager only

B: The client

C: HSE inspectors

D: Everyone on site

General Responsibilities

1.11

A risk assessment tells you:

☐ A: who has created the risks

☐ B: what legislation should be applied

☐ C: the generic risks associated with the construction industry

☐ D: what risks may exist and how they should be dealt with

1.12

The Health and Safety at Work Act places legal duties on:

☐ A: employers only

☐ B: operatives only

☐ C: all people at work

☐ D: self-employed people only

1.13

Why do you need to know the health and safety Regulations that deal with your type of work?

☐ A: They tell you how to write risk assessments

☐ B: They explain how health and safety is managed on your site

☐ C: They tell you when HSE inspections will take place

☐ D: They place legal duties on you

1.14

Who is responsible for managing health and safety on construction sites?

☐ A: The company safety officer

☐ B: The HSE

☐ C: The client

☐ D: The site manager

1.15

You will often hear the word hazard mentioned. What does it mean?

☐ A: Anything that can cause harm

☐ B The level of risk on site

☐ C: A type of barrier or machine guard

☐ D: All of the other answers

1.16

A whole site has been issued with a Prohibition Notice. During the period that the notice applies, what does this mean?

- [ ] A: The site manager should be on site before work starts
- [ ] B: The site manager must check with the HSE before starting work
- [ ] C: No one must use any survey equipment, tools or machinery
- [ ] D: All work must stop on site until the safety problem is rectified

1.17

Why is the Health and Safety at Work Act important to anyone at work? Give **two** answers.

- [ ] A: It tells you which aspects of site work are dangerous
- [ ] B: It must be learned before anyone can start work
- [ ] C: It requires all employers to provide a safe place to work
- [ ] D: It sets out how work should be carried out
- [ ] E: It puts legal duties on employees with regard to their acts or omissions

1.18

It is important for those at work to see their employer's health and safety policy because it tells them:

- [ ] A: how to do their job safely
- [ ] B: how to write risk assessments
- [ ] C: how health and safety is managed within their organisation
- [ ] D: how to use tools and equipment safely

1.19

Under the Construction (Design and Management) Regulations, who has responsibility for appointing a competent CDM Co-ordinator?

- [ ] A: All duty holders
- [ ] B: The client
- [ ] C: Any contractor
- [ ] D: The principal contractor

1.20

If a designer appoints another designer or a contractor, the Construction (Design and Management) Regulations require them to:

- [ ] A: agree production and payment terms
- [ ] B: ensure that they attend the site induction
- [ ] C: be sure that they carry out their duties under the regulations
- [ ] D: be satisfied that they are competent

1.21

Under the Construction (Design and Management) Regulations, who has the responsibility for ensuring that project arrangements are in place for the allocation of sufficient resources?

- [ ] A: The CDM Co-ordinator
- [ ] B: The Client
- [ ] C: The Lead Designer
- [ ] D: The Principal Contractor

1.22

In what circumstances must a construction phase plan be prepared?

- [ ] A: Whenever the Construction (Design and Management) Regulations apply
- [ ] B: Only if the client requires one
- [ ] C: Only if it is a contractual requirement
- [ ] D: Whenever the project is notifiable under the CDM Regs

1.23

Who is responsible for the management of health and safety on site?

- [ ] A: The client
- [ ] B: The designers
- [ ] C: The principal contractor
- [ ] D: The CDM Co-ordinator

1.24

In meeting the risk management objectives of the Construction (Design and Management) Regulations, which statement summarises the best project attitude for improving health and safety on construction sites?

- [ ] A: Only the CDM co-ordinator can eliminate hazards
- [ ] B: Only the client has the budget to eliminate hazards
- [ ] C: Designers and contractors can eliminate hazards
- [ ] D: Designers create hazards and contractors eliminate them

1.25

Initially, who is most likely to hold most information about the health and safety constraints of the site?

- [ ] A: The CDM Co-ordinator
- [ ] B: The principal contractor
- [ ] C: The Health and Safety Executive
- [ ] D: The client

Answers: 1.21 = B, 1.22 = D, 1.23 = C, 1.24 = C, 1.25 = D

1.26

Who is responsible for managing health and safety on site?

- [ ] A: The CDM Co-ordinator
- [ ] B: The principal contractor
- [ ] C: The client
- [ ] D: The designer

1.27

What is the critical reason for supplying health or safety information?

- [ ] A: To comply with procedures
- [ ] B: It is a requirement of the role of the CDM Co-ordinator
- [ ] C: To ensure that all risks are identified and managed
- [ ] D: To satisfy the Health and Safety Executive

1.28

The design team has agreed with the client to omit reference to asbestos in a work package even though asbestos is present in the structure. In this circumstance the design team and the client have acted:

- [ ] A: reasonably practicably
- [ ] B: illegally
- [ ] C: legally
- [ ] D: with adequate regard

1.29

What is likely to be the most effective way of informing site workers about residual health and safety risks?

- [ ] A: Adding notes to the specification
- [ ] B: Supplying material safety data sheets
- [ ] C: Adding notes to drawings
- [ ] D: Notes in a bill of quantities

1.30

As a summary of the general principles of prevention, ERIC stands for:

- [ ] A: Employ, Reduce, Inform, Control
- [ ] B: Ensure, Reduce, Inform, Control
- [ ] C: Eliminate, Reduce, Inform, Control
- [ ] D: Educate, Reduce, Inform, Control

General Responsibilities

1.31

What is the most effective method to prevent workers falling from height while carrying out construction and maintenance work?

- [ ] A: Leave the decisions on how to work at height to the Principal Contractor
- [ ] B: Ensure details of risky operations are included in the construction phase health and safety plan
- [ ] C: Educate the workforce to be more careful while working at height
- [ ] D: Ensure that design and construction solutions eliminate the need for working at height

1.32

Which of the following does **not** eliminate significant construction hazards?

- [ ] A: Working at height from an elevating platform
- [ ] B: Rerouting a service run to avoid an asbestos panel
- [ ] C: Pre-cast holding down bolts
- [ ] D: Waiting for a shared occupancy building to become empty before construction work starts

1.33

Which of the following has the highest priority under the principles of prevention and protection?

- [ ] A: Specifying the use of a mobile elevating work platform for steel erection
- [ ] B: Pre-fabrication of steelwork that eliminates the need for a high-level bolted connection
- [ ] C: The installation of a 2 metre high barrier to prevent unauthorised access to an area where work at height is taking place
- [ ] D: The introduction of a comprehensive briefing sheet to warn workers of the dangers of working at height

1.34

Under the general principles of prevention, which of the following provides the least effective protection of construction workers?

- [ ] A: The use of an elevating mobile platform to prevent working from ladders
- [ ] B: The provision of information about working at height to enable the contractor to give instructions to the workers
- [ ] C: The pre-fabrication of steelwork that prevents working at height but introduces a lifting operation
- [ ] D: A change to a high level steelwork connection detail that reduces by 50% the time taken to make the connection

Answers: 1.31 = D, 1.32 = A, 1.33 = B, 1.34 = B

1.35

Under the general principles of prevention, what is generally accepted as providing the **most** effective protection for construction workers?

- [ ] A: Construction processes which protect groups of workers rather than individuals

- [ ] B: Contractors having information on residual risks to enable them to give instructions to their workers

- [ ] C: Changes that replace dangerous construction processes with less dangerous ones

- [ ] D: Design and construction processes that eliminate hazards

1.36

Assuming all other factors are equal, in terms of resources and risk exposure, which of the following provides the solution with the lowest risk?

- [ ] A: A two-person operation to inspect a structure once every 2 years

- [ ] B: A two-person operation to inspect a structure once a year

- [ ] C: A four-person operation to inspect a structure every 6 months

- [ ] D: A one-person operation to inspect a structure every month

1.37

Which of the following, taken on their own, provides the **best** solution for reducing risks related to site transport and access?

- [ ] A: Provide all site staff with information detailing the site layout and designated traffic routes

- [ ] B: A one-way traffic system complete with segregated pedestrian routes

- [ ] C: Ensure that there are adequate signs directing traffic to the various parts of the site

- [ ] D: Reduce the need for some vehicle movements on site by requiring more materials to be off-loaded manually outside the site

1.38

While on site you observe the following techniques and processes which are used to manage risk; which of them is the **least effective** in reducing health or safety risks on site?

- [ ] A: Off-site prefabrication of building components

- [ ] B: Significantly reducing the need for deep excavations

- [ ] C: Reducing the need for work at height

- [ ] D: Specifying the PPE to be provided to everyone on site

1.39

Which one of the following is **not** a relevant option for reducing the risk to construction workers?

- A: Reduce the number of workers involved in an operation
- B: Reduce the exposure of site workers to risk
- C: Reduce the cost of work equipment
- D: Reduce the frequency of an activity

1.40

When visiting a structure built in the last 10 years, where would you expect to find information about the risks associated with the completed structure?

- A: The construction phase plan
- B: Operation and maintenance manuals
- C: The original project specification
- D: The health and safety file

1.41

Historically, what has been the main cause of death on construction sites?

- A: Electrocution
- B: Drowning
- C: Falls from height
- D: Weil's disease (Leptospirosis)

1.42

Which of the following health risks has resulted in the death of the most construction workers?

- A: Hand-arm vibration
- B: Hard wood dust
- C: Weil's disease (Leptospirosis)
- D: Asbestos

1.43

Which of the following is generally considered the most significant construction risk?

- A: Being struck by moving vehicles
- B: Noise
- C: Drowning
- D: Electricity

1.44

Which of the following is a good reason for obtaining and communicating information on construction health risks?

- A: Many site visitors do not know enough about construction health risks
- B: Construction workers do not always understand the long-term effects on their health of particular construction processes
- C: Ill health in construction workers is more common than traumatic injuries
- D: All of the other answers

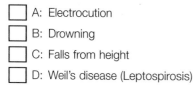
Answers: 1.39 = C, 1.40 = D, 1.41 = C, 1.42 = D, 1.43 = A, 1.44 = D

1.45

Which sector of the construction industry generally has the highest fatal accident incident rate?

- [ ] A: Civil engineering sites
- [ ] B: Demolition sites
- [ ] C: Green field sites
- [ ] D: Maintenance and refurbishment sites

1.46

Under the Construction (Design and Management) Regulations the duty to apply the principles of prevention rests with which duty holders?

- [ ] A: Designers and Clients
- [ ] B: Contractors and Principal contractors
- [ ] C: The CDM Co-ordinator
- [ ] D: All duty holders

1.47

The Construction (Design and Management) Regulations require Contractors and Designers to only commence work if:

- [ ] A: clients are supplied with information about the Client's duties under the CDM Regulations
- [ ] B: their contracts with clients address the Client's obligations under the CDM Regulations
- [ ] C: the Health and Safety Executive is notified of the project before a design is prepared
- [ ] D: clients are aware of the Client's duties under the CDM Regulations before design work is started

1.48

You plan to visit a site that you know is notifiable and you realise that a CDM Co-ordinator has not been appointed; what should you do?

- [ ] A: Contact the Client immediately and ensure that they are aware of their duties
- [ ] B: Work to the Client's brief
- [ ] C: Complete all work within your brief and ignore the lack of a CDM Co-ordinator
- [ ] D: Stop all work on the project immediately and notify the HSE

Accident Prevention and Reporting

2.1

Which of these does not have to be recorded in the accident book?

- [ ] A: The injured person's national insurance number
- [ ] B: The date and time of the accident
- [ ] C: Details of the injury
- [ ] D: The home address of the injured person

2.2

A scaffold has collapsed and you saw it happen. When you are asked about the accident, you should say:

- [ ] A: nothing, you are not a scaffold expert
- [ ] B: as little as possible because you don't want to get people into trouble
- [ ] C: exactly what you saw
- [ ] D: who you think is to blame and how they should be punished

2.3

What is the most important reason for keeping a working area on a construction site clean and tidy?

- [ ] A: To prevent slips, trips and falls
- [ ] B: So that the workers don't have to have a big clean-up at the end of the week
- [ ] C: So that waste skips can be emptied more often
- [ ] D: To recycle waste and help the environment

2.4

If you have a minor accident, who should report it?

- [ ] A: Anyone who saw the accident happen
- [ ] B: A contractor
- [ ] C: You
- [ ] D: The HSE

2.5

How would you expect to find out about site health and safety rules when you first arrive on site?

- [ ] A: During site induction
- [ ] B: By reading the project file before going to site
- [ ] C: By reading your employer's health and safety policy
- [ ] D: By asking others on the site

Answers: 2.1 = A, 2.2 = C, 2.3 = A, 2.4 = C, 2.5 = A

2.6

A near miss is an incident where:

A: you were just too late to see what happened

B: someone could have been injured

C: someone was injured and nearly had to go to hospital

D: someone was injured and nearly had to take time off work

2.7

If you cut your finger and it won't stop bleeding, you should:

A: wrap something around it and carry on working

B: tell the site manager

C: wash it clean then carry on working

D: find a first-aider or get other medical help

2.8

When leaving site you notice that a contractor is working in an unsafe manner. What should you do?

A: It is not your responsibility so go back to your office

B: Return and speak to the site manager

C: Contact the CDM Co-ordinator

D: Contact the contractor's head office

2.9

If your doctor says that you have Weil's disease contracted from a site visit, you will need to tell your employer. Why?

A: Your employer has to warn your colleagues not to go anywhere near you

B: Your employer will have to report it to the HSE

C: Your work colleagues might catch it from you

D: The site on which you contracted it will have to be closed down

2.10

Why is it important to attend site induction?

A: You will get to know other new starters

B: Risk assessments will be handed out

C: Site specific health and safety rules will be explained

D: Permits to Work will be handed out

2.11

While on site you see a contractor working in a way that presents an imminent danger to yourself and others around you. What should you do immediately?

- [ ] A: Move to another area of the site and continue with your work
- [ ] B: Before you leave site ensure that you inform the site manager
- [ ] C: Speak directly to the site operatives and ask them to stop work and then tell the site manager
- [ ] D: Ensure that you inform the client and the CDM Co-ordinator

2.12

When must you record an accident in the accident book?

- [ ] A: If you are injured in any way
- [ ] B: Only if you have to be off work
- [ ] C: Only if you have suffered a broken bone
- [ ] D: Only if you have to go to hospital

2.13

If someone is injured at work, who should record it in the accident book?

- [ ] A: The site manager, and no one else
- [ ] B: The injured person, or someone acting for them
- [ ] C: The first-aider, and no one else
- [ ] D: Someone from the HSE

2.14

Why is it important to report all accidents?

- [ ] A: It might stop them happening again
- [ ] B: Some types of accident have to be reported to the HSE
- [ ] C: Details have to be entered in the accident book
- [ ] D: All of the other answers

2.15

Why is it important to report **all near miss** incidents?

- [ ] A: The HSE needs to know about everything that happens on site
- [ ] B: Because it is required by the Reporting of Injuries Diseases and Dangerous Occurrences Regulations (RIDDOR)
- [ ] C: It is a requirement of the CDM Regulations
- [ ] D: To learn from them and stop them happening again

2.16

You can help prevent accidents by:

- [ ] A: reporting unsafe working conditions
- [ ] B: becoming a first-aider
- [ ] C: knowing where the first aid-kit is kept
- [ ] D: knowing how to get help quickly

2.17

When are people working on, or visiting, construction sites most likely to have an accident?

- [ ] A: In the morning
- [ ] B: In the afternoon
- [ ] C: During the summer months
- [ ] D: When they first start on any new site

2.18

Historically, which type of accident **kills** the most construction workers?

- [ ] A: Falling from height
- [ ] B: Contact with electricity
- [ ] C: Being run over by site transport
- [ ] D: Being hit by a falling object

2.19

Which of these helps everyone work safely on site?

- [ ] A: Site induction
- [ ] B: Toolbox talks
- [ ] C: Risk assessments and method statements
- [ ] D: All the other answers

3.1

Direct sunlight on bare skin can cause:

- [ ] A: dermatitis
- [ ] B: rickets
- [ ] C: acne
- [ ] D: skin cancer

3.2

When site workers need to handle a hazardous substances they should wear the correct gloves to help stop:

- [ ] A: skin disease
- [ ] B: vibration white finger
- [ ] C: Raynaud's syndrome
- [ ] D: arthritis

3.3

Your doctor has given you some medication. Which of these questions is the **most** important?

- [ ] A: Will it make me sleepy or unsafe to work?
- [ ] B: Will the medication make me work more slowly?
- [ ] C: Will my manager need to be told?
- [ ] D: Will it cause me to oversleep and be late for work?

3.4

Someone goes to the pub at lunchtime and has a couple of pints of beer. What should they do next?

- [ ] A: Drink plenty of strong coffee then go back to work
- [ ] B: Stay away from the site for the rest of the day
- [ ] C: Stay away for an hour and then go back to work
- [ ] D: Eat something, wait 30 minutes and then go back to work

3.5

Exposure to engine oil and other mineral oils can cause:

- [ ] A: skin problems
- [ ] B: heart disease
- [ ] C: breathing problems
- [ ] D: vibration white finger

Answers: 3.1 = D, 3.2 = A, 3.3 = A, 3.4 = B, 3.5 = A

3.6

You can get occupational dermatitis from:

☐ A: hand-arm vibration

☐ B: another person with dermatitis

☐ C: some types of strong chemical

☐ D: sunlight

3.7

You can catch an infection called **tetanus** from contaminated land or water. How does it get into your body?

☐ A: Through your nose when you breathe

☐ B: Through an open cut in your skin

☐ C: Through your mouth when you eat or drink

☐ D: It doesn't, it only infects animals and not people

3.8

Exposure to which of the following may **not** result in lung disease?

☐ A: Asbestos

☐ B: Bird droppings

☐ C: Steam

☐ D: Silica dust

3.9

Pigeon droppings and nests are found in an area where you are required to work. You should:

☐ A: carry on with your work carefully

☐ B: stop work and seek advice

☐ C: try to catch the pigeons

☐ D: let them fly away before carrying on with your work

3.10

Very dirty hands should be cleaned with:

☐ A: soap and water

☐ B: thinners

☐ C: white spirit

☐ D: paraffin

Health and Welfare

3.11

In order to keep rats away from site, site management should:

- A: buy rat traps and put them around the site
- B: ask the local authority to put down rat poison
- C: provide a site cat
- D: ensure that scraps of food are not left lying about and that food is disposed of properly

3.12

You find that toilets on site are dirty. What should you do?

- A: Ignore the problem, it is normal
- B: Make sure that you tell the site manager who can sort it out
- C: Ask someone to find some cleaning materials and to attend to it
- D: See if you can use the toilets in a nearby café or pub

3.13

You are more likely to catch Weil's disease (Leptospirosis) if you:

- A: work near wet ground, waterways or sewers
- B: work near air conditioning units
- C: work on building refurbishment
- D: drink water from a standpipe

3.14

Breathing in a dusty atmosphere for long periods can cause:

- A: occupational asthma
- B: occupational dermatitis
- C: skin cancer
- D: Weil's disease

3.15

White spirit or other solvents should not be used to clean hands because:

- A: they strip the protective oils from the skin
- B: they remove the top layer of skin
- C: they block the pores of the skin
- D: they carry harmful bacteria that attack the skin

3.16

Which of the following is a legal requirement for the site welfare facilities?

- A: There is wholesome drinking water
- B: Somewhere to take a rest
- C: Suitable and sufficient lighting
- D: All of the other answers

Answers: 3.11 = D, 3.12 = B, 3.13 = A, 3.14 = A, 3.15 = A, 3.16 = D

3.17

The site toilets do not flush. What should you do?

- [ ] A: Try not to use the toilets while you are at work
- [ ] B: Tell the site manager about the problem
- [ ] C: Try to fix the fault yourself
- [ ] D: Ask a plumber to fix the fault

3.18

While carrying out a survey on site you may be working in an area where two kinds of animal can carry a disease called Leptospirosis in their urine. Which two?

- [ ] A: Cat
- [ ] B: Sheep
- [ ] C: Rat
- [ ] D: Rabbit
- [ ] E: Cow

3.19

Look at these statements about illegal drugs in the workplace. Which one is true in relation to site work?

- [ ] A: Users of illegal drugs are a danger to everyone
- [ ] B: People who take illegal drugs work better and faster
- [ ] C: People who take illegal drugs take fewer days off work
- [ ] D: Taking illegal drugs is a personal choice so other people shouldn't worry about it

3.20

If you get a hazardous substance on your hands, it can pass from your hands to your mouth when you eat. Give **two** ways to stop this.

- [ ] A: Wear protective gloves when you are working
- [ ] B: Wash your hands before eating
- [ ] C: Put barrier cream on your hands before eating
- [ ] D: Wear protective gloves then turn them inside-out before eating
- [ ] E: Wash your work gloves then put them on again before eating

3.21

The early signs of Weil's disease (Leptospirosis) can be easily confused with:

- [ ] A: dermatitis
- [ ] B: diabetes
- [ ] C: hayfever
- [ ] D: influenza ('flu)

3.22

When visiting a site you find that there is nowhere for you to wash your hands. What should you do?

- [ ] A: Wait until you get home then wash them
- [ ] B: Go to a local café or pub and use the washbasin in their toilet
- [ ] C: Speak to the site manager about the problem
- [ ] D: Bring your own hand washing equipment in future

3.23

What sort of rest area should be provided for operatives on site?

- [ ] A: A covered area
- [ ] B: A covered area and some chairs
- [ ] C: A covered area, tables and chairs, and something to heat water
- [ ] D: Nothing, contractors don't have to provide rest areas

3.24

What is the **minimum** that should be provided on site for washing hands?

- [ ] A: Nothing, there is no need to provide washing facilities
- [ ] B: Running hot water and electric hand-dryers
- [ ] C: A cold water standpipe and paper towels
- [ ] D: Hot and cold water (or warm water), soap and a way to dry hands

3.25

Why should you not just rely on barrier cream to protect your skin from harmful substances?

- [ ] A: There may be none available on site
- [ ] B: Many harmful substances go straight through it
- [ ] C: It is difficult to wash off
- [ ] D: It can irritate your skin

3.26

Occupational asthma is a disease that can end someone's working life. It can be caused by:

- [ ] A: exposure to loud noise
- [ ] B: exposure to rat urine
- [ ] C: skin contact with any hazardous substance
- [ ] D: breathing in certain dust, fumes or vapours

Answers: 3.22 = C, 3.23 = C, 3.24 = D, 3.25 = B, 3.26 = D

4.1

To lift a load, you should always try to:

- [ ] A: stand with your feet together when lifting
- [ ] B: bend your back when lifting
- [ ] C: carry the load away from your body, at arm's length
- [ ] D: divide large loads into smaller loads

4.2

You need to lift a load from the floor. You should stand with your:

- [ ] A: feet together, legs straight, back bent
- [ ] B: feet together, knees bent in a deep squatting position
- [ ] C: feet slightly apart, one leg slightly forward, knees flexed
- [ ] D: feet wide apart, legs straight, back bent

4.3

To lift a load safely, you need to think about:

- [ ] A: its size and condition
- [ ] B: its weight
- [ ] C: whether it has handholds
- [ ] D: all of the other answers

4.4

When you lift a load manually, you must:

- [ ] A: slightly curve your back and sufficiently flex your hips and knees
- [ ] B: make sure there are always two people to lift the load
- [ ] C: use a crane or another lifting device to pick up the load
- [ ] D: move the load as quickly as possible

4.5

Your new job involves some manual handling of survey equipment in and out of vehicles. An old injury means that you have a weak back. What should you do?

- [ ] A: If you take care there is no need to inform your manager
- [ ] B: Tell your manager that lifting might be a problem
- [ ] C: Try some lifting then tell your manager about your back
- [ ] D: Only tell your manager about your back if it gets injured again

Answers: 4.1 = D, 4.2 = C, 4.3 = D, 4.4 = A, 4.5 = B

4.6

If you have to twist or turn your body when you lift and place a load, it means:

- ☐ A: the weight you can lift safely is **less** than usual
- ☐ B: the weight you can lift safely is **more** than usual
- ☐ C: nothing, you can lift the **same** weight as usual
- ☐ D: you **must** wear a back brace

4.7

You have been asked to move a load that might be too heavy for you. You cannot divide it into smaller parts and there is no one to help you. What should you do?

- ☐ A: Do not move the load until you have found a safe method
- ☐ B: Ask someone to get a forklift truck, even though you suspect they can't drive one
- ☐ C: You know how to lift, so try to lift it using the correct lifting methods
- ☐ D: Get on and lift and move the load quickly as this helps avoid injury

4.8

Who should decide what weight can be lifted safely?

- ☐ A: The person performing the lift
- ☐ B: Their manager
- ☐ C: Their employer
- ☐ D: The site manager

4.9

Under the regulations for manual handling, **all** employees must:

- ☐ A: wear back-support belts when lifting anything
- ☐ B: make a list of all the heavy things they have to carry
- ☐ C: lift any size of load once the risk assessment has been done
- ☐ D: follow the requirements of their employer's safe systems of work

4.10

If manual lifting activities are part of a task. What must the employer do?

- ☐ A: Make sure the lifting operations are supervised
- ☐ B: Carry out a risk assessment of the task
- ☐ C: Nothing, as it is part of some work operations to lift loads
- ☐ D: Watch while the load is lifted

4.11

Someone has to move a load while they are sitting, not standing. How much can they move safely?

- ☐ A: Less than usual
- ☐ B: The usual amount
- ☐ C: Twice the usual amount
- ☐ D: Three times the usual amount

Answers: 4.6 = A, 4.7 = A, 4.8 = A, 4.9 = D, 4.10 = B, 4.11 = A

5.1

How many people are allowed to be on a ladder at the same time?

- [ ] A: 2
- [ ] B: 1
- [ ] C: 1 on each section of an extension ladder
- [ ] D: 3 if it is long enough

5.2

A scaffold guard-rail must be removed to allow you to carry out a survey. You are not a scaffolder. Can you remove the guard-rail?

- [ ] A: Yes, if you put it back as soon as you have finished
- [ ] B: Yes, if you put it back before you leave site
- [ ] C: No, only a scaffolder can remove the guard-rail but you can put it back
- [ ] D: No, only a scaffolder can remove the guard-rail and put it back

5.3

Who should check a ladder before it is used?

- [ ] A: The person who is going to use it
- [ ] B: A site supervisor
- [ ] C: The site safety officer
- [ ] D: The manufacturer

5.4

What is the **best** way to make sure that a ladder is secure and won't slip?

- [ ] A: Ensure that it is tied at the top
- [ ] B: Ask someone to stand with their foot on the bottom rung
- [ ] C: Tie it at the bottom
- [ ] D: Ask for the bottom of the ladder to be wedged with blocks of wood

5.5

You need access to inspect a pitched roof. It is not possible for the contractor to install fall prevention. What should you do?

- [ ] A: Hold onto something while you use your other hand to make notes
- [ ] B: Ask someone to hold on to you while you make notes
- [ ] C: If you have been trained, wear a harness and lanyard and fix it to an anchor point
- [ ] D: Tie a rope round your waist and tie the other end to an anchor point

5.6

Which of the following is NOT an appropriate indicator that a scaffold is safe to use?

- A: An up-to-date inspection log
- B: Joint inspection with a competent person
- C: Up-to-date scafftag
- D: Other people are using it

5.7

Before you climb any ladder on site you should make sure that it is:

- A: aluminium
- B: hired
- C: secured
- D: painted

5.8

To ensure the safety of people who have to gain access to a place of work at height, ladders are:

- A: always acceptable for work below 2 metres
- B: alright to use if it gets the job done more quickly
- C: generally the least favoured option
- D: now banned on all sites

5.9

Which of these statements is correct? Work at height is:

- A: only work carried out above 2 metres
- B: only work carried out on a scaffold
- C: banned under the Work at Height Regulations
- D: to be avoided where possible

5.10

If you see an unguarded opening in a floor whilst you are on site, what is your first priority?

- A: Stop any work going on around it and immediately report it to the site manager
- B: Ensure the opening is where it should be on the drawings
- C: Measure the opening and check it against the bill of quantities
- D: Nothing: work on site is the sole responsibility of the contractor

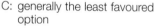

Answers: 5.6 = D, 5.7 = C, 5.8 = C, 5.9 = D, 5.10 = A

5.11

Whilst visiting a site, what action should you take if something falls from a scaffolding, nearly hitting you?

A: Gain access to the scaffold and investigate the problem

B: Do not walk near that part of the scaffolding again

C: Ensure you are wearing your hard hat

D: Immediately clear other people from the area and report the near-miss to the site manager

5.12

Your organisation's policy is to avoid walking on fragile roof materials. A common example of fragile roof material is:

A: asphalt felt roof

B: asbestos cement sheets and rooflights

C: raised seam roofs

D: single-ply membrane

5.13

You are required to inspect some roofwork. Which of the following provides effective protection against falls when roofwork is underway?

A: Only using experienced operatives

B: Workers staying away from the edge of the roof

C: Edge of the roof clearly marked with flicker tape

D: Suitable edge protection in place

5.14

If a working platform is 4 metres above the ground, the foot of the access ladder should be placed:

A: 1 metre out

B: 2 metres out

C: 3 metres out

D: 4 metres out

5.15

To ensure your safety and that of the site workers, what should the contractor include in a safety method statement for working at height? Give **three** answers.

- A: The cost of the job and time it will take
- B: The sequence of operations and the equipment to be used
- C: How much insurance cover will be required
- D: How falls are to be prevented
- E: Who will supervise the job on site

5.16

To ensure your safety when carrying out an inspection at height, tower scaffolds may be erected by:

- A: anyone who has the instruction book
- B: anyone who is competent and authorised
- C: advanced scaffolders only
- D: an employee of the hire company only

5.17

To ensure your safety when using a scaffold to carry out an inspection at height, a competent person must routinely inspect the scaffold:

- A: before it is first used and then at intervals not exceeding 7 days
- B: only after it has been erected
- C: after it is erected and then at monthly intervals
- D: after it is erected and then at intervals not exceeding 10 days

5.18

You are required to carry out a joint inspection of an industrial roof with the contractor. When covering rooflights, in order to prevent falls, what **two** requirements should the contractor ensure that the covers meet?

- A: They are made from the same material as the roof covering
- B: They are made from clear material to allow the light through
- C: They are strong enough to take the weight of any load placed on it
- D: They are waterproof and windproof
- E: They are fixed in position to stop them being dislodged

Answers: 5.15 = B,D,E, 5.16 = B, 5.17 = A, 5.18 = C,E

5.19

What is the **main** reason for using a safety net or other soft-landing system rather than a personal fall-arrest system?

- [ ] A: Soft-landing systems are cheaper to use and do not need inspecting
- [ ] B: It is always easy to rescue workers who fall into a soft-landing system
- [ ] C: Specialist knowledge is not required to install soft-landing systems
- [ ] D: Soft-landing systems are collective fall arrest measures

5.20

What is the **main** reason for reporting to the site manager that debris has been allowed to gather in safety nets?

- [ ] A: It will overload the net
- [ ] B: It looks untidy from below
- [ ] C: It could injure someone who falls into the net
- [ ] D: Small pieces of debris may fall through the net

5.21

You are working at height taking site measurements, but the securing cord for a safety net is in your way. What should you do?

- [ ] A: Untie the cord, carry out your work and tie it up again
- [ ] B: Untie the cord, but ask the contractor to re-tie it when you have finished
- [ ] C: Tell the contractor that you are going to untie the cord
- [ ] D: Leave the cord alone and report the problem to the contractor

5.22

For maximum protection from being injured through falling, a safety net should be rigged:

- [ ] A: immediately below where you or site workers are working
- [ ] B: 2 metres below where you or site workers are working
- [ ] C: 6 metres below where you or site workers are working
- [ ] D: at any height below the working position

5.23

What is the **main** danger of leaving someone suspended in a harness for too long after they have fallen?

- A: They will become bored
- B: They may try to climb back up the structure and fall again
- C: They may suffer severe trauma or even death
- D: It is a distraction for other workers

5.24

As part of a feasibility study you are planning an inspection of roof trusses inside a factory building. What is the recommended **maximum** height for a free-standing mobile tower when used indoors?

- A: There is no height restriction
- B: Three lifts
- C: As specified by the manufacturer
- D: Three times the longest base dimension

5.25

After gaining access to the platform of a mobile tower, the **first** thing you should do is:

- A: check that the tower's brakes are locked on
- B: check that the tower has been correctly assembled
- C: close the access hatch to stop people or equipment from falling
- D: check that the tower does not rock or wobble

5.26

Edge protection is designed to:

- A: make access to the roof easier
- B: secure tools and materials close to the edge
- C: stop rainwater running off the roof onto workers below
- D: prevent people and materials falling

5.27

Before climbing a ladder you notice that it has a rung missing near the top. What should you do?

A: Do not use the ladder and report the defect immediately

B: Use the ladder but take care when stepping over the position of the missing rung

C: Ask for the ladder to be turned over so that the missing rung is near the bottom and use it

D: Ask the contractor to make an improvised repair by lashing something across the stiles

5.28

When can someone who is not a scaffolder remove parts of a scaffold?

A: If the scaffold is not more than 2 lifts in height

B: As long as a scaffolder refits the parts after the work has finished

C: Never, only competent scaffolders can remove the parts

D: Only if it is a tube and fittings scaffold

5.29

How far should a ladder extend above the stepping-off point if there is no alternative, firm hand-hold?

A: 3 rungs

B: 2 rungs

C: 1 metre

D: Half a metre

5.30

When using ladders for access, what is the **maximum** vertical distance between landings?

A: 5 metres

B: There is no maximum

C: 9 metres

D: 30 metres

5.31

On a working platform, the **maximum** permitted gap between the guard-rails is:

A: 350 mm

B: 470 mm

C: 490 mm

D: 510 mm

5.32

When should guard-rails be fitted to a working platform?

A: If it is possible to fall 2 metres

B: At any height if a fall could result in an injury

C: If it is possible to fall 3 metres

D: Only if materials are being stored on the working platform

5.33

A 'Class 3' ladder is:

A: for domestic use only and must not be used on site

B: of industrial quality and can be used safely

C: a ladder that has been made to a European Standard

D: made of insulating material and can be used near to overhead cables

5.34

How will you know the maximum weight or number of people that can be lifted safely on a mobile elevating work platform?

A: The weight limit is reached when the platform is full

B: It will say on the Health and Safety Law poster

C: You will be told during site induction

D: From an information plate fixed to the machine

5.35

When is it most appropriate to use a safety harness and lanyard for working at height?

A: Only when the roof has a steep pitch

B: Only when crossing a flat roof with clear roof-lights

C: Only when all other options for fall prevention have been ruled out

D: Only when materials are stored at height

5.36

When is it safe to use a scissor lift on soft ground?

A: When the ground is dry

B: When the machine can stand on scaffold planks laid over the soft ground

C: When stabilisers or outriggers can be deployed onto solid ground

D: Never

Answers: 5.32 = B, 5.33 = A, 5.34 = D, 5.35 = C, 5.36 = C

5.37

You need to cross a roof. How do you establish if it is fragile?

- A: Tread gently and listen for cracking
- B: Look at the risk assessment or method statement
- C: Look at the roof surface and make your own assessment
- D: There is no need to do so if you walk along a line of bolts

5.38

Before gaining access to a roof, you notice some overhead cables that may be within reach. What should you do?

- A: Go onto the roof anyway but keep away from them while you work but remember they are there
- B: Confirm with whoever is in charge of the site that it is safe for you to be on the roof
- C: Make sure that you are provided with access via a wooden ladder
- D: Ask for coloured bunting to be hung from them to remind everyone that they are there

5.39

Having been trained to use a harness, while trying to clip your lanyard to an anchor point, you find the locking device does not work. What should you do?

- A: Carry on working and report it later
- B: Tie the lanyard in a knot round the anchor
- C: Stop work and report it to your manager
- D: Just carry on working without it

5.40

Which of the following is a significant disadvantage of using an aluminium scaffold tower?

- A: The aluminium will corrode in wet weather
- B: It can never be built more than 2 lifts high
- C: Materials cannot be stored on the working platform
- D: The lack of weight means it can be displaced by high winds

5.41

If someone is working from a cherry-picker, they should attach their safety lanyard to:

- A: a strong part of the structure that they are working on
- B: a secure anchorage point inside the platform
- C: a secure point on the boom of the machine
- D: a scaffold guard-rail

5.42

When work is being carried out above public areas, your first consideration should be to:

- A: minimise the number of people below at any one time
- B: provide alternative routes for the public and keep them away from the area
- C: let the public know what you are doing
- D: provide netting to prevent falling objects

5.43

What should be the **first** consideration of a cherry-picker operator should the wind speed increase significantly?

- A: To tie all lightweight objects to the hand-rails of the basket
- B: To decide whether the machine will remain stable
- C: To tie the cherry picker basket to the structure being worked upon
- D: To clip their lanyard to the structure being worked upon

5.44

While carrying out a site visit you see someone who is working above a safety net system that has a damaged net. What should you do?

- A: Ask them to work somewhere away from the damaged area of net
- B: Ask them to stop work and report it to the site manager
- C: Ask them to tie the damaged edges together using the net test cords
- D: Ask them to go and see if they can get hold of a harness and lanyard

Answers: 5.41 = B, 5.42 = B, 5.43 = B, 5.44 = B

5.45

If a fall-restraint lanyard has damaged stitching, the user should:

A: use the lanyard if the damaged stitching is less than 2 inches long

B: get a replacement lanyard

C: not use the damaged lanyard and work without one

D: use the lanyard if the damaged stitching is less than 6 inches long

5.46

Which of these **must** happen before any roof work starts?

A: A risk assessment must be carried out

B: Those working on the roof must be trained in the use of safety harnesses

C: Permits to Work must be issued to those allowed to work on the roof

D: A weather forecast must be obtained

5.47

A cherry picker has been hired-in to carry out a particular job. When fully extended it does not quite reach the required height. What would you expect the operator to do?

A: Use a step-ladder balanced on the machine platform

B: Extend the machine fully and stand on the guard-rails

C: Abandon the machine and use a long extending ladder

D: Not to carry out the job until a safe alternative means of access has been established

5.48

A MEWP is being used to carry out work at height. What is the only circumstance in which it is acceptable to lower the platform using the ground-level controls?

A: When the person using the ground-level controls is competent to do so

B: In an emergency

C: If the person working on the platform needs to step off the MEWP to gain access to the high-level work area

D: If the person working on the platform needs both hands free to carry out the job in hand

5.49

While undertaking a site visit you see that work is being carried out at height; which of these is the safest way to transfer waste materials to ground level? The contractor to:

- [ ] A: provide a waste chute directly into a skip appropriate for the purpose
- [ ] B: keep the area clear of people and then to throw the waste down
- [ ] C: erect barriers around the area where the waste will land
- [ ] D: bag or bundle up the waste before throwing it down

5.50

An outdoor tower scaffold has stood overnight in high winds and heavy rain. What should be done before you use the scaffold to carry out an inspection?

- [ ] A: Test that the brakes still work
- [ ] B: Tie the scaffold to the adjacent structure
- [ ] C: Ensure that the scaffold is inspected by a competent person
- [ ] D: Ensure that the platform hatch still works correctly

5.51

Scaffold inspections should be undertaken by:

- [ ] A: you when you visit site
- [ ] B: a competent person
- [ ] C: someone who has attended a 'Scaffold Appreciation' course
- [ ] D: a scaffold company employee only

5.52

Which of the following provides the public with adequate protection from falling objects?

- [ ] A: Clear warning signs
- [ ] B: A worker in a hi-vis vest standing on the footway to warn people
- [ ] C: Viewing panels in the site hoarding
- [ ] D: A fan or scaffold 'tunnel' over the footway

5.53

All work at height must be:

- [ ] A: risk assessed and properly planned
- [ ] B: only undertaken by scaffold contractors
- [ ] C: carried out as quickly as possible
- [ ] D: suspended if the forecast wind speed is above Force 2

Answers: 5.49 = A, 5.50 = C, 5.51 = B, 5.52 = D, 5.53 = A

5.54

Which of the following might form **part of** a safe method of work to cross a fragile roof?

- [ ] A: Walk along the line of bolts
- [ ] B: It's OK if you cannot see fragile roof signs
- [ ] C: Don't walk on any plastic panels
- [ ] D: Use crawling boards

5.55

You are inspecting a flat roof. What is the best way to stop yourself and others from falling over the edge?

- [ ] A: Have a large warning sign placed at the edge of the roof
- [ ] B: Ask someone to keep watch and to shout out when someone gets too close to the edge
- [ ] C: Ask for the edge to be protected with a guard-rail and toe-board
- [ ] D: Ask for red and white tape to mark the edge

5.56

A ladder should **not** be painted because:

- [ ] A: the paint will make it slippery to use
- [ ] B: the paint may hide any damaged parts
- [ ] C: the paint could damage the metal parts of the ladder
- [ ] D: it will need regular re-painting

5.57

You need to use a ladder to reach a work platform. What should be the slope or angle of the ladder?

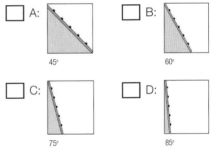

- [ ] A: 45°
- [ ] B: 60°
- [ ] C: 75°
- [ ] D: 85°

5.58

You are working above deep water. There is a risk of falling and it is not practicable to provide fall-prevention measures. Which **two** items of PPE do you need?

- [ ] A: Wellington boots
- [ ] B: Harness/lanyard system
- [ ] C: Life jacket
- [ ] D: Waterproof jacket
- [ ] E: Waterproof trousers

5.59

You need to use a ladder to get to a scaffold platform. Which of these statements is **true**?

- [ ] A: It must be tied and extend about five rungs above the platform
- [ ] B: All broken rungs must be clearly marked
- [ ] C: It must be wedged at the bottom to stop it slipping
- [ ] D: Two people must be on the ladder at all times to provide stability

5.60

What is the **best** way to stop people falling through fragile roof lights?

- [ ] A: Ask for everyone to be told where the roof lights are
- [ ] B: The roof lights to be covered with something that can take the weight of a person
- [ ] C: The roof lights to be covered with netting
- [ ] D: The roof lights to be marked with red and white tape

5.61

In order to carry out a site inspection you need to use a mobile tower scaffold. You notice that the wheel brakes do not work. What should you do?

- [ ] A: Ask someone to wedge the wheels to stop them moving
- [ ] B: Do not use the tower
- [ ] C: Only use the tower if the floor is level
- [ ] D: Get someone to hold the tower while you use it

5.62

When you climb a ladder, you must:

- [ ] A: have three points of contact with the ladder at all times
- [ ] B: have two points of contact with the ladder at all times
- [ ] C: use a safety harness
- [ ] D: have two people on the ladder at all times

5.63

 What does this sign mean?

- [ ] A: Do not run on the roof
- [ ] B: Slippery when wet
- [ ] C: Fragile roof
- [ ] D: Load-bearing roof

Answers: 5.59 = A, 5.60 = B, 5.61 = B, 5.62 = A, 5.63 = C

5.64

When materials are stored on a working platform, the site manager must make sure:

- [ ] A: the materials are secure, even in windy weather
- [ ] B: the platform can take the weight of the materials
- [ ] C: the materials do not make the platform unsafe for others
- [ ] D: all of the other answers

5.65

You need to reach the working platform of a mobile tower scaffold. What is the right way to do this?

- [ ] A: Climb up the tower frame on the outside of the tower
- [ ] B: Lean a ladder against the tower and climb up that
- [ ] C: Only use a ladder built into the tower
- [ ] D: Climb from the rigid structure on which you are standing

5.66

A mobile tower scaffold must **not** be used on:

- [ ] A: soft or uneven ground
- [ ] B: a paved patio
- [ ] C: an asphalt road
- [ ] D: a smooth concrete path

5.67

In law you are working at height when you could fall from:

- [ ] A: the first lift of a scaffold or higher
- [ ] B: 2 metres above the ground or higher
- [ ] C: any height that would cause an injury if you fell
- [ ] D: 3 metres above the ground or higher

5.68

You find a ladder that is damaged. What should you do?

- [ ] A: Don't let anyone use it and immediately inform the site manager about the damage
- [ ] B: Don't use it but report the damage when you have finished your site visit
- [ ] C: Ask someone to try and mend the damage
- [ ] D: Use the ladder if you can avoid the damaged part

5.69

When could a ladder be used as a safe place of work?

- [ ] A: If it is no longer than 4 metres
- [ ] B: If no other working platform is immediately available
- [ ] C: If other people do not need to use it for access
- [ ] D: If you are doing light work for a short time

Answers: 5.64 = D, 5.65 = C, 5.66 = A, 5.67 = C, 5.68 = A, 5.69 = D

6.1

When should you wear safety boots or safety shoes on site?

- A: Only when you work at ground level
- B: In the winter
- C: Only when it is cold and wet
- D: All the time

6.2

To get the **maximum** protection from your safety helmet, you should wear it:

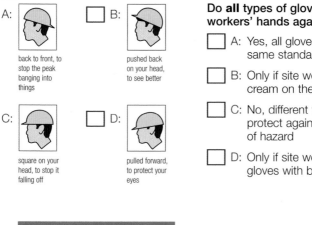

- A: back to front, to stop the peak banging into things
- B: pushed back on your head, to see better
- C: square on your head, to stop it falling off
- D: pulled forward, to protect your eyes

6.3

If your PPE gets damaged, you should:

- A: throw it away and work without it
- B: stop what you are doing until it is replaced
- C: carry on wearing it but work more quickly
- D: try to repair it

6.4

While on site you observe that there is a risk of materials flying into site workers' eyes. What should they be wearing in order to protect themselves?

- A: Tinted welding goggles
- B: Laser safety glasses
- C: Chemical-resistant eye protection
- D: Impact-resistant eye protection

6.5

Do **all** types of glove protect site workers' hands against chemicals?

- A: Yes, all gloves are made to the same standard
- B: Only if site workers put barrier cream on their hands as well
- C: No, different types of glove protect against different types of hazard
- D: Only if site workers cover their gloves with barrier cream

Answers: 6.1 = D, 6.2 = C, 6.3 = B, 6.4 = D, 6.5 = C

6.6

You have been given a **dust mask** to protect you against hazardous fumes in the work area. What should you do?

- [ ] A: Do not go into the work area until you have the correct respiratory protective equipment
- [ ] B: Go into the work area but try to get the job done quickly
- [ ] C: Go into the work area but take frequent breaks
- [ ] D: Ask for a second dust mask to wear on top of the first one

6.7

You are about to enter an active work area on site. How will you know if you need any extra PPE?

- [ ] A: By looking at your employer's health and safety policy
- [ ] B: You will just be expected to know
- [ ] C: From the risk assessment or method statement
- [ ] D: A letter will be sent to your office

6.8

Who has the legal duty to ensure that employees are provided with any PPE they need?

- [ ] A: Their employer
- [ ] B: The employees who need it
- [ ] C: The client for the project
- [ ] D: The person whose design created the need for the use of PPE

6.9

You have to work outdoors in bad weather. Your employer should supply you with waterproof clothing because:

- [ ] A: it will have the company name and logo on it
- [ ] B: you are less likely to get muscle strains if you are warm and dry
- [ ] C: you are less likely to catch Weil's disease if you are warm and dry
- [ ] D: the site manager will be able to see you more clearly in the rain

6.10

When should eye protection be worn?

- [ ] A: On very bright, sunny days
- [ ] B: If there is a risk of eye injury
- [ ] C: When it has been included in the bill of quantities
- [ ] D: Only for work with chemicals

6.11

Look at these statements about PPE. Which one is **not true**? Employees must:

- A: pay for any damage or loss
- B: store it correctly when not using it
- C: report any damage or loss to their manager
- D: use it as instructed

6.12

What features should you be looking for when obtaining Wellington boots for a site visit?

- A: They must be black with a good sole pattern
- B: They only need a steel toe-cap
- C: They must have a steel toe-cap and mid sole
- D: They must be smooth-soled to prevent the transfer of contaminated materials

6.13

You must wear high visibility clothing:

- A: when the need is identified in the contractor's or your employer's site rules
- B: only if you are inspecting deep excavations or tunnels
- C: during normal daylight hours only
- D: only if you are working alongside moving plant

6.14

You must wear head protection on site **at all times unless** you are:

- A: self-employed
- B: working alone
- C: in a safe area, like the site office
- D: working in very hot weather

6.15

Your employer **must** supply PPE:

- A: twice a year
- B: if employees pay for it
- C: if it is in the contract
- D: if it is needed to provide protection

6.16

Do employees have to pay for any PPE they need?

- A: Yes, they must pay for all of it
- B: Only to replace lost or damaged PPE
- C: Yes, but they only have to pay half the cost
- D: No, the employer must pay for it

Answers: 6.11 = A, 6.12 = C, 6.13 = A, 6.14 = C, 6.15 = D, 6.16 = D

6.17 ▬▬▬▬▬▬▬

If you drop your safety helmet from height on to a hard surface, you should:

☐ A: have any cracks repaired then carry on wearing it

☐ B: make sure there are no cracks then carry on wearing it

☐ C: work without a safety helmet until you can get a new one

☐ D: stop work and get a new safety helmet

6.18 ▬▬▬▬▬▬▬

In order to carry out a structural inspection you need to wear a full body harness. You have never used one before. What must happen before you start work?

☐ A: Your employer must provide you with information, competent advice and training

☐ B: Ask someone wearing a similar harness to show you what to do

☐ C: Try to work it out for yourself

☐ D: Read the instruction book and follow any advice that it contains

7.1

If you think someone has a broken leg, you should:

A: lie them on their side in the recovery position

B: use your belt to strap their legs together

C: send for the first aider or get other help

D: lie them on their back

7.2

If someone gets some grit in their eye, the best thing you can do is:

A: hold the eye open and wipe it with clean tissue paper

B: ask them to rub the eye until it starts to water

C: tell them to blink a couple of times

D: hold the eye open and flush it with clean water

7.3

Someone gets a large splinter in their hand. It is deep under the skin and it hurts. What should you do?

A: Use something sharp to dig it out

B: Make sure they get first aid

C: Tell them to ignore it and let the splinter come out on its own

D: Try to squeeze out the splinter with your thumbs

7.4

Someone has fallen from height and has no feeling in their legs. You should tell them to:

A: roll onto their back and keep their legs straight

B: roll on to their side and bend their legs

C: stay where they are until medical help arrives

D: raise their legs to see if any feeling comes back

7.5

Someone has got a nail in their foot. You are not a first aider. You must not pull out the nail because:

A: you will let air and bacteria get into the wound

B: the nail is helping to reduce the bleeding

C: it will prove that the casualty was not wearing safety boots

D: the nail would become a bio-hazard

7.6

This sign means:

A: first aid

B: safe to cross

C: no waiting

D: wait here for help

Answers: 7.1 = C, 7.2 = D, 7.3 = B, 7.4 = C, 7.5 = B, 7.6 = A

7.7

You will find out about emergency assembly points from:

- [ ] A: a risk assessment
- [ ] B: a method statement
- [ ] C: the site induction
- [ ] D: the Permit to Work

7.8

If someone burns their hand, the **best** thing you can do is:

- [ ] A: put the hand into cold water
- [ ] B: tell them to carry on working to exercise the hand
- [ ] C: rub barrier cream or Vaseline into the burn
- [ ] D: wrap your handkerchief around the burn

7.9

You have to carry out a survey on a remote unoccupied site. What should your employer provide you with?

- [ ] A: A small first aid kit
- [ ] B: The first aid box out of the office
- [ ] C: Nothing
- [ ] D: A book on first aid

7.10

When would you expect eye-wash bottles to be provided?

- [ ] A: **Only** on demolition sites where asbestos has to be removed
- [ ] B: **Only** on sites where refurbishment is being carried out
- [ ] C: On all sites where people could get something in their eyes
- [ ] D: On all sites where showers are needed

7.11

If someone is in contact with a live cable, the **best** thing you can do is:

- [ ] A: phone the electricity company
- [ ] B: dial 999 and ask for an ambulance
- [ ] C: switch off the power and call for help
- [ ] D: pull them away from the cable

7.12

What is the **first** thing you should do if you find an injured person?

- [ ] A: Tell the site manager
- [ ] B: Check that you are not in any danger
- [ ] C: Move the injured person to a safe place
- [ ] D: Ask the injured person what happened

Answers: 7.7 = C, 7.8 = A, 7.9 = A, 7.10 = C, 7.11 = C, 7.12 = B

7.13

Someone working in a deep manhole has collapsed. What is the **first** thing you should do?

- [ ] A: Get someone lowered into the manhole on a rope
- [ ] B: Climb into the manhole and give mouth-to-mouth resuscitation
- [ ] C: Run and tell the site manager
- [ ] D: Raise the alarm by shouting to let others know what has happened

7.14

How do you find out what to do if you are injured on site?

- [ ] A: By asking someone on site
- [ ] B: By looking for the first aid sign
- [ ] C: By attending a first aid course
- [ ] D: You should be told at site induction

7.15

In what way are site-based staff and visitors informed of the location of first-aid facilities on site?

- [ ] A: By walking the site looking for the first-aid sign
- [ ] B: By searching the site office
- [ ] C: They should be told during site induction
- [ ] D: By reading the Health and Safety Law poster

7.16

In which way should site visitors be informed of the actions to take in the event of an on-site emergency?

- [ ] A: They should study the plans on the wall of the site office
- [ ] B: They are informed during site induction
- [ ] C: They should ask the site manager
- [ ] D: They should take a look around the site for the emergency assembly point

7.17

How can you see for yourself that attention has been given to simple emergency procedures on site?

- [ ] A: Scaffolding has inspection lables fitted
- [ ] B: The distance between the structure and the assembly point is minimised
- [ ] C: Fire points with extinguishers and a means of raising the alarm are in position
- [ ] D: All electrical appliances have been electrically tested

7.18

If your employer's policy is that all staff who visit sites carry a travelling first-aid kit, it **must not** contain:

- [ ] A: bandages
- [ ] B: plasters
- [ ] C: safety pins
- [ ] D: pain killers

7.19

Someone collapses with stomach pain. There is no first aider on site. What should you do first?

- [ ] A: Get them to sit down
- [ ] B: Get someone to call the emergency services
- [ ] C: Get them to lie down in the recovery position
- [ ] D: Give them some pain killers

7.20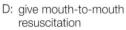

If someone falls and is knocked unconscious, you should first:

- [ ] A: turn them over so they are lying on their back
- [ ] B: send for medical help
- [ ] C: slap their face to wake them up
- [ ] D: give mouth-to-mouth resuscitation

7.21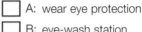

 This sign means:

- [ ] A: wear eye protection
- [ ] B: eye-wash station
- [ ] C: risk of splashing
- [ ] D: shower block

7.22

This sign means:

- [ ] A: one-way system
- [ ] B: public right of way
- [ ] C: assembly point
- [ ] D: site transport route

7.23

It is your employer's policy that when undertaking a site survey one member of the survey team should be a trained first aider. What is the one thing a first aider **cannot** do?

- [ ] A: Give mouth-to-mouth resuscitation
- [ ] B: Stop any bleeding
- [ ] C: Give medicines without authorisation
- [ ] D: Treat casualties if they are unconscious

7.24

Do those in charge of sites have to provide a first-aid box?

- [ ] A: Yes, every site must have one
- [ ] B: **Only** if more than 50 people work on site
- [ ] C: **Only** if more than 25 people work on site
- [ ] D: No, there is no legal duty to provide one

7.25

How should you be informed about the emergency arrangements? Give **two** answers.

- [ ] A: From the site induction
- [ ] B: From the site notice boards
- [ ] C: Ask the HSE
- [ ] D: Ask the local hospital
- [ ] E: Look in the H&S file

7.26

If there is an emergency while you are on site, you should first:

- [ ] A: leave the site and go back to your office
- [ ] B: phone your office
- [ ] C: follow the site emergency procedure
- [ ] D: phone the police

Answers: 7.24 = A, 7.25 = A,B, 7.26 = C

8.1

Which of these statements about asbestos is **true**?

- [ ] A: Brown asbestos is safe but blue asbestos is a hazard to health
- [ ] B: White asbestos is safe to use
- [ ] C: All types of asbestos are safe to handle
- [ ] D: All types of asbestos are a hazard to health

8.2

These safety signs are displayed where hazardous substances are stored. Which sign means **corrosive substance**?

- [ ] A:
- [ ] B:
- [ ] C:
- [ ] D:

8.3

These safety signs are displayed where hazardous substances are stored. Which sign means **toxic substance**?

- [ ] A:
- [ ] B:
- [ ] C:
- [ ] D:

8.4

These safety signs are displayed where hazardous substances are stored. Which sign means **harmful substance**?

- [ ] A:
- [ ] B:
- [ ] C:
- [ ] D:

8.5

You find a bottle of chemicals. The bottle does not have a label. What is the **first** thing you should do?

- [ ] A: Smell the chemical to see what it is
- [ ] B: Put it in a bin to get rid of it
- [ ] C: Move it to somewhere safe
- [ ] D: Ensure that it remains undisturbed and report it

8.6

How can you tell if a product is hazardous?

- [ ] A: By a symbol on the container label
- [ ] B: By the shape of the container
- [ ] C: It will always be in a black container
- [ ] D: It will always be in a cardboard box

8.7

A COSHH assessment tells you how:

- [ ] A: to lift heavy loads and how to protect yourself
- [ ] B: to work safely in confined spaces
- [ ] C: a substance might harm you and how to protect yourself
- [ ] D: noise levels are assessed and how to protect your hearing

8.8

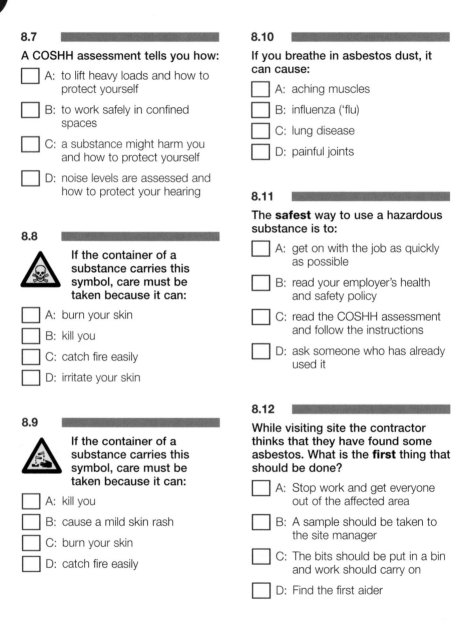

If the container of a substance carries this symbol, care must be taken because it can:

- [ ] A: burn your skin
- [ ] B: kill you
- [ ] C: catch fire easily
- [ ] D: irritate your skin

8.9

If the container of a substance carries this symbol, care must be taken because it can:

- [ ] A: kill you
- [ ] B: cause a mild skin rash
- [ ] C: burn your skin
- [ ] D: catch fire easily

8.10

If you breathe in asbestos dust, it can cause:

- [ ] A: aching muscles
- [ ] B: influenza ('flu)
- [ ] C: lung disease
- [ ] D: painful joints

8.11

The **safest** way to use a hazardous substance is to:

- [ ] A: get on with the job as quickly as possible
- [ ] B: read your employer's health and safety policy
- [ ] C: read the COSHH assessment and follow the instructions
- [ ] D: ask someone who has already used it

8.12

While visiting site the contractor thinks that they have found some asbestos. What is the **first** thing that should be done?

- [ ] A: Stop work and get everyone out of the affected area
- [ ] B: A sample should be taken to the site manager
- [ ] C: The bits should be put in a bin and work should carry on
- [ ] D: Find the first aider

Answers: 8.7 = C, 8.8 = B, 8.9 = C, 8.10 = C, 8.11 = C, 8.12 = A

8.13

When a contractor is assessing the risk of using a substance that he believes to be hazardous, he should **first:**

- [ ] A: review the material safety data sheet
- [ ] B: ensure that safe storage is available on site
- [ ] C: ensure that workers are provided with respiratory equipment
- [ ] D: ensure workers are trained to use respiratory equipment

8.14

Which of these statements apply to asbestos? It is:

- [ ] A: harmful to health
- [ ] B: fibrous mineral
- [ ] C: likely to be found in buildings built between 1950-1999
- [ ] D: all the other answers

8.15

You are visiting a site where an active asbestos removal enclosure has been set up. Which of the following would indicate that it is operating efficiently?

- [ ] A: Appropriate signage
- [ ] B: Everyone to be wearing red suits
- [ ] C: The sides of the enclosure bowing in
- [ ] D: Everyone is wearing respiratory protective equipment

8.16

You are visiting a project that involves removing paint from old iron-work. Which of the following would enable the contractor to assess the foreseeable health risk of the work during the tender period?

- [ ] A: Lab-test results of a sample of paint giving lead content
- [ ] B: The prevailing wind conditions
- [ ] C: Fit testing of respiratory protective equipment
- [ ] D: Tests to determine the average paint thickness

8.17

You are visiting a site where flooring is being stuck down by a lone worker, using a liquid adhesive in a small inner room that has no visible means of ventilation. For what reason might you quickly bring this to the attention of the site manager?

- [ ] A: It is illegal for anyone to work on their own
- [ ] B: The work should be carried out under a hot-work permit
- [ ] C: Kneeling and working is bad for his back
- [ ] D: The vapours from the adhesive may be a health hazard without sufficient fresh air

Answers: 8.13 = A, 8.14 = D, 8.15 = C, 8.16 = A, 8.17 = D

8.18

The COSHH regulations deal with:

- A: the safe use of tools and equipment
- B: the safe use of lifting equipment
- C: the safe use of hazardous substances
- D: safe working at height

8.19

When this safety sign is displayed on the storage area for hazardous substances, it indicates that the substance is:

- A: harmful
- B: toxic
- C: corrosive
- D: an irritant

8.20

When this safety sign is displayed on the storage area for hazardous substances, it indicates that the substance is:

- A: harmful
- B: toxic
- C: corrosive
- D: an irritant

8.21

If the container of a substance carries this symbol, care must be taken because it can (give **two** answers):

- A: catch fire easily
- B: irritate your skin
- C: harm your health
- D: kill you
- E: cause burns

8.22

Which of these does **not** cause skin problems?

- A: Lead
- B: Bitumens
- C: Epoxy resins
- D: Solvents

8.23

Which of these will give you health and safety information about a hazardous substance?

- A: The site diary
- B: The delivery note
- C: The COSHH assessment
- D: The accident book

8.24

How should contractors dispose of hazardous waste from site?

- [ ] A: It should be put in any skip on site

- [ ] B: In accordance with the waste management plan

- [ ] C: It should be buried on site

- [ ] D: It should be taken to the nearest local authority waste tip

8.25

You are arranging for an intrusive survey to be carried out. You suspect that asbestos may be present. What level of information should you look for?

- [ ] A: A Type 3 asbestos survey

- [ ] B: A Type 1 asbestos survey

- [ ] C: A Type 2 asbestos survey

- [ ] D: A certificate of reoccupation

Electrical Safety and Hand Tools

9.1

It is safe to work close to an overhead power line if:

- [ ] A: you do not touch the line
- [ ] B: you use a wooden ladder
- [ ] C: there is a clear indication that the power is switched off
- [ ] D: it is not raining

9.2

This warning sign means:

- [ ] A: risk of electrocution
- [ ] B: risk of radiation
- [ ] C: electrical appliance
- [ ] D: risk of lightning

9.3

The colour of a 110 volt power cable and connector should be:

- [ ] A: black
- [ ] B: red
- [ ] C: blue
- [ ] D: yellow

9.4

A residual current device (RCD) must be used in conjunction with 230 volt electrical equipment because:

- [ ] A: it lowers the voltage
- [ ] B: it quickly cuts off the power if there is a fault
- [ ] C: it makes the tool run at a safe speed
- [ ] D: it saves energy and lowers costs

9.5

How could a site worker check if the residual current device (RCD) through which a 230 volt hand tool is connected to the supply is working correctly?

- [ ] A: Switch the tool on and off
- [ ] B: Press the test button on the RCD unit
- [ ] C: Switch the power on and off
- [ ] D: Run the tool at top speed to see if it cuts out

9.6

Why do building sites use a 110 volt electricity supply instead of the usual 230 volt domestic supply?

- [ ] A: It is cheaper
- [ ] B: It is less likely to kill people
- [ ] C: It moves faster along the cables
- [ ] D: It is safer for the environment

Answers: 9.1 = C, 9.2 = A, 9.3 = D, 9.4 = B, 9.5 = B, 9.6 = B

9.7

What is the significance of a yellow plug and a yellow supply cable fitted to an electrical hand tool?

- [ ] A: The tool runs off a 110 volt supply
- [ ] B: The tool is waterproof and can be used outdoors in wet conditions
- [ ] C: The tools runs off a 240 volt supply and should not be used on site
- [ ] D: The tool has been PAT tested within the past 12 months

9.8

For an enhanced level of personal safety, electrical tools on a site should **not** be:

- [ ] A: 230 volt
- [ ] B: PAT tested
- [ ] C: CE marked
- [ ] D: serviceable

9.9

Someone near you is using a disc cutter to cut concrete blocks. What **three** immediate hazards are likely to affect you?

- [ ] A: Flying fragments
- [ ] B: Dermatitis
- [ ] C: Dust in the air
- [ ] D: High noise levels
- [ ] E: Skin cancer

9.10

Someone near you is using a laser level. What health hazard is likely to affect you?

- [ ] A: Skin cancer
- [ ] B: None if it is used correctly
- [ ] C: Gradual blindness
- [ ] D: Burning of the skin, similar to sunburn

9.11

Most cutting and grinding machines have guards. What are the **two** main functions of the guard?

- [ ] A: To stop materials getting onto the blade or wheel
- [ ] B: To give the operator a firm handhold
- [ ] C: To balance the machine
- [ ] D: To stop fragments flying into the air
- [ ] E: To stop the operator coming into contact with the blade or wheel

9.12

On building sites, the recommended safe voltage for electrical equipment is:

- [ ] A: 12 volts
- [ ] B: 24 volts
- [ ] C: 110 volts
- [ ] D: 230 volts

9.13

Which two of the following would you expect to find on a PAT test label?

☐ A: When the next safety check is due

☐ B: When the equipment was made

☐ C: Who tested the equipment before it left the factory

☐ D: Its earth-loop impedance

☐ E: When the equipment was last tested as being safe to use

Answers: 9.13 = A,E

10.1

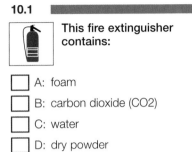

This fire extinguisher contains:

- ☐ A: foam
- ☐ B: carbon dioxide (CO2)
- ☐ C: water
- ☐ D: dry powder

10.2

A fire assembly point is the place where:

- ☐ A: fire engines must go when they arrive on site
- ☐ B: the fire extinguishers are kept
- ☐ C: people must go when the fire alarm sounds
- ☐ D: the fire started

10.3

This fire extinguisher contains:

- ☐ A: water
- ☐ B: foam
- ☐ C: dry powder
- ☐ D: carbon dioxide (CO2)

10.4

If you discover a fire, the **first** thing you should do is:

- ☐ A: put any equipment away
- ☐ B: finish what you are doing if it is safe to do so
- ☐ C: try to put out the fire
- ☐ D: raise the alarm

10.5

If you hear the fire alarm, you should go to:

- ☐ A: the site entrance
- ☐ B: the assembly point
- ☐ C: the site car park
- ☐ D: the fire

10.6

WATER

This extinguisher must **not** be used on:

- ☐ A: electrical fires
- ☐ B: wood fires
- ☐ C: burning furniture
- ☐ D: burning clothes

10.7

If you see 'frost' around the valve on an LPG cylinder, it means:

- [ ] A: the cylinder is nearly empty
- [ ] B: the cylinder is full
- [ ] C: the valve is leaking
- [ ] D: you must lay the cylinder on its side

10.8

If there is a fire, you will need to go to the site assembly point. How would you expect to find out where this is?

- [ ] A: During a visit by the HSE
- [ ] B: During site induction
- [ ] C: By reading your employer's health and safety policy
- [ ] D: Your colleagues will tell you

10.9

Which **two** extinguishers are best for putting out oil fires?

- [ ] A:
  FOAM
- [ ] B:
  CARBON DIOXIDE
- [ ] C:
  DRY POWDER
- [ ] D:
  WATER

10.10

WATER

This water type of fire extinguisher puts out a fire by:

- [ ] A: starving the fire of oxygen
- [ ] B: cooling the burning material
- [ ] C: increasing the oxygen supply
- [ ] D: diluting the oxygen with another gas

10.11

For safety reasons LPG cylinders used for heating the site cabin must be:

- [ ] A: located outside the cabin
- [ ] B: located inside the cabin but away from the heat source
- [ ] C: connected to the heat source by flexible rubber tubing
- [ ] D: laid on their side

10.12

You would expect to see highly flammable materials being stored:

- [ ] A: under the site manager's desk
- [ ] B: against the hoarding furthest away from the site offices
- [ ] C: in a secure compound in the open air
- [ ] D: in the timber store

Answers: 10.7 = C, 10.8 = B, 10.9 = A,C, 10.10 = B, 10.11 = A, 10.12 = C

10.13

As a result of risk assessment work is to be carried out under a hot-work permit. The permit must specify that the work is:

- [ ] A: carried out at a time when the site is otherwise unoccupied
- [ ] B: completed immediately before the end of the working day
- [ ] C: completed in time for any resultant fire to be discovered and dealt with and at least one hour before the site closes
- [ ] D: completed one hour after the permit expires

10.14

Acetylene and oxygen cylinders that are not in use are being stored together outside a meeting room. In the interests of everyone's safety they should be:

- [ ] A: kept on a bottle trolley together
- [ ] B: stored separately and away from site accommodation
- [ ] C: laid down so that they cannot fall over and damage the valves
- [ ] D: stored together but away from site accommodation

10.15

When installing a fuel-oil storage area, the contractor must include:

- [ ] A: water type fire extinguishers
- [ ] B: suitable bunding
- [ ] C: hand-washing facilities
- [ ] D: a porous ground surface to absorb spillage

10.16

CARBON DIOXIDE

How does a CO2 extinguisher put out fires?

- [ ] A: It gets rid of the heat
- [ ] B: It keeps out oxygen
- [ ] C: It removes the fuel
- [ ] D: It makes the fire wet

10.17

To put out an oil fire, you must **not** use:

- [ ] A:

  FOAM
- [ ] B:

  CARBON DIOXIDE
- [ ] C: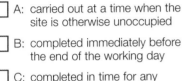

  DRY POWDER
- [ ] D:

  WATER

10.18

When a carbon dioxide (CO_2) fire extinguisher is used, the nozzle gets:

- [ ] A: very cold
- [ ] B: very hot
- [ ] C: warm
- [ ] D: very heavy

10.19

All fires need **heat, fuel** and **oxygen**. Knowing this, explain how a water extingisher puts out a wood fire.

- [ ] A: By removing the oxygen
- [ ] B: By smothering the flames
- [ ] C: By removing the fuel
- [ ] D: By cooling the fuel

10.20

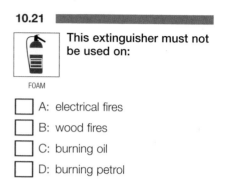

WATER

This extinguisher can be used to put out:

- [ ] A: burning oil
- [ ] B: electrical fires
- [ ] C: wood fires
- [ ] D: burning petrol

10.21

This extinguisher must not be used on:

FOAM

- [ ] A: electrical fires
- [ ] B: wood fires
- [ ] C: burning oil
- [ ] D: burning petrol

10.22

Which **two** extinguishers can be used on electrical fires?

- [ ] A: DRY POWDER
- [ ] B: FOAM

- [ ] C: WATER
- [ ] D: CARBON DIOXIDE

10.23

Work is taking place in a corridor that is a fire escape route. The contractor must ensure that:

- [ ] A: tools and equipment do not block the route
- [ ] B: all doors into the corridor are locked
- [ ] C: only spark-proof tools are used
- [ ] D: all fire escape signs are removed before work starts

Answers: 10.18 = A, 10.19 = D, 10.20 = C, 10.21 = A, 10.22 = A,D, 10.23 = A

11.1

Which sign means flammable substance?

A:

B:

C:

D:

11.2

This sign means:

A: wear ear protection if you want to

B: you must wear ear protection

C: you must not make a noise

D: caution, noisy machinery

11.3

Fire exit signs are coloured:

A: blue and white

B: red and white

C: green and white

D: red and yellow

11.4

Fire point

This sign tells you where:

A: to go if there is a fire

B: fire extinguishers should be kept

C: a fire will start

D: flammable materials should be kept

11.5

This sign means:

A: press here to sound the fire alarm

B: do not touch

C: wear hand protection

D: press here to switch on the emergency light

11.6

This sign means:

A: press here to sound the fire alarm

B: fire hose reel

C: turn key to open

D: do not use if there is a fire

11.7

This sign means:

- [ ] A: danger from radiation
- [ ] B: danger from bright lights or lasers
- [ ] C: caution, poor lighting
- [ ] D: you must wear eye protection

11.8

Which sign means 'Warning, laser beams'?

- [ ] A:
- [ ] B:
- [ ] C:
- [ ] D:

11.9

This sign means:

- [ ] A: no access onto the scaffold
- [ ] B: no entry without full PPE
- [ ] C: no entry for people on foot
- [ ] D: no entry during the day

11.10

Green and white signs mean:

- [ ] A: you **must** do something
- [ ] B: you **must not** do something
- [ ] C: hazard or danger
- [ ] D: safe condition, emergency escape route or first aid

11.11

Blue and white signs mean:

- [ ] A: you **must** do something
- [ ] B: you **must not** do something
- [ ] C: hazard or danger
- [ ] D: safe condition

11.12

Yellow and black signs mean:

- [ ] A: you **must** do something
- [ ] B: you **must not** do something
- [ ] C: hazard or danger
- [ ] D: safe condition

Answers: 11.7 = D, 11.8 = D, 11.9 = C, 11.10 = D, 11.11 = A, 11.12 = C

11.13

Round, red and white signs with a diagonal line mean:

- A: you **must** do something
- B: you **must not** do something
- C: hazard or danger
- D: safe condition

11.14

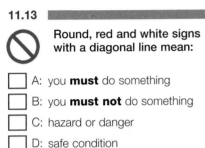

This sign means:

- A: plant operators wanted
- B: forklift trucks operating
- C: manual handling not allowed
- D: storage area

11.15

If you see this sign on a scaffold, you should:

- A: remove the access ladder
- B: only work on the first lift
- C: stay off the scaffold because it is not safe
- D: only use a MEWP to get on to the scaffold

11.16

This sign means:

- A: you must wear safety boots
- B: you must wear wellington boots
- C: caution, slip and trip hazards
- D: wear safety boots if you want to

11.17

This sign means:

- A: caution, cold materials
- B: caution, hot materials
- C: carry out work using one hand
- D: you must wear safety gloves

11.18

If you see this sign, you must:

- A: wear white clothes at night
- B: wear high visibility clothes
- C: do nothing, it only applies to managers
- D: wear wet weather clothes

11.19

A crane has to do a difficult lift. The signaller asks you to help, but you are not trained in plant signals. What should you do?

A: Politely refuse because you don't know how to signal

B: Start giving signals to the crane driver

C: Only help if the signaller really can't manage alone

D: Ask the signaller to show you what signals to use

11.20

A truck has to tip materials into a trench. Who should give signals to the truck driver?

A: Anyone who is there

B: Someone standing in the trench

C: Anyone who knows the signals

D: Anyone who is trained and appointed for the job

11.21

This sign means:

A: leaking roof

B: wear waterproof clothes

C: emergency shower

D: fire sprinklers

11.22

If you see this sign on a scaffold, it means

A: do not run

B: no escape route

C: fire door

D: fire escape route

11.23

If you see this sign on a scaffold, it means

A: harmful

B: toxic

C: corrosive

D: dangerous to the environment

Answers: 11.19 = A, 11.20 = D, 11.21 = C, 11.22 = B, 11.23 = D

12.1

Which **two** of the following conditions would you expect a site manager to apply in order to manage the risk of site staff operating plant?

- [ ] A: The plant operative must be competent
- [ ] B: The plant operative must be authorised
- [ ] C: The plant operative must be over 21 years old
- [ ] D: The plant operative must hold a full driving licence
- [ ] E: The plant operative must hold a UK passport

12.2

You need to walk past someone using a mobile crane. You should:

- [ ] A: guess what the crane operator will do next and squeeze by
- [ ] B: try to catch the attention of the crane operator
- [ ] C: run to get past the crane quickly
- [ ] D: take another route so that you stay clear of the crane

12.3

You need to walk past a 360° mobile crane. The crane is operating near a wall. What is the **main** danger?

- [ ] A: The crane could crash into the wall
- [ ] B: You could be crushed if you walk between the crane and the wall
- [ ] C: Whole-body vibration from the crane
- [ ] D: High noise levels from the crane

12.4

You are walking across the site. A large mobile crane reverses across your path. What should you do?

- [ ] A: Help the driver to reverse
- [ ] B: Start to run so that you can pass behind the reversing crane
- [ ] C: Pass close to the front of the crane
- [ ] D: Wait or find another way around the crane

12.5

If you see a dumper being driven too fast, you should:

- [ ] A: keep out of its way and report the matter to the site manager
- [ ] B: try to catch the dumper and speak to the driver
- [ ] C: report the matter to the police
- [ ] D: do nothing, dumpers are allowed to go above the site speed limit

12.6

When is site transport allowed to drive along a pedestrian route?

- [ ] A: During meal breaks
- [ ] B: If it is the shortest route
- [ ] C: Only if necessary and if all pedestrians are excluded
- [ ] D: Only if the vehicle has a flashing yellow light

12.7

You see a lorry parking. It has a flat tyre. Why should you tell the site manager?

- [ ] A: The lorry will use more fuel
- [ ] B: The lorry will need to travel at a much slower speed
- [ ] C: The lorry is unsafe to drive
- [ ] D: The lorry can only carry small loads

12.8

While observing an excavator digging a trial pit you notice that liquid is dripping and forming a small pool under the back of the machine. What could this mean?

- [ ] A: It is normal for fluids to vent after the machine stops
- [ ] B: The machine is hot so the diesel has expanded and overflowed
- [ ] C: Someone put too much diesel into the machine before it started work
- [ ] D: The machine has an hydraulic fluid leak and could be unsafe

12.9

You see a driver refuelling an excavator. Most of the diesel is spilling on to the ground. What is the first thing you should do?

- [ ] A: Tell the site manager the next time you see them
- [ ] B: Tell the driver immediately and then report this to the site manager
- [ ] C: Look for a spillage kit immediately
- [ ] D: Do nothing, the diesel will eventually seep into the ground

12.10

How would you expect a well-organised site to keep pedestrians away from traffic routes?

- [ ] A: The site manager will direct all pedestrians away from traffic routes
- [ ] B: The traffic routes will be shown on the Health and Safety Law poster
- [ ] C: There will be barriers between traffic and pedestrian routes
- [ ] D: There is no need to keep traffic and pedestrians apart

12.11

A site vehicle is **most** likely to injure pedestrians when it is:

- [ ] A: reversing
- [ ] B: lifting materials onto scaffolds
- [ ] C: tipping into an excavation
- [ ] D: digging out footings

12.12

You must **not** walk behind a lorry when it is reversing because:

- [ ] A: most lorries are not fitted with mirrors
- [ ] B: the driver is unlikely to know you are there
- [ ] C: most lorry drivers aren't very good at reversing
- [ ] D: you will need to run, not walk, to get past it in time

12.13

The quickest way to where you want to be on site is through a contractor's vehicle compound. Which route should you take?

- [ ] A: Around the compound if vehicles are moving
- [ ] B: Straight through the compound if no vehicles appear to be moving
- [ ] C: Around the compound every time
- [ ] D: Straight through the compound if no-one is looking

12.14

How would you expect to be told about the site traffic rules?

- [ ] A: During site induction
- [ ] B: By an HSE inspector
- [ ] C: By a note on a notice board
- [ ] D: In a letter sent to your office

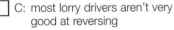

Answers: 12.10 = C, 12.11 = A, 12.12 = B, 12.13 = C, 12.14 = A

12.15

A forklift truck is blocking the way to where you want to go on site. It is lifting materials on to a scaffold. What should you do?

- A: Only walk under the raised load if you are wearing a safety helmet
- B: Catch the driver's attention and then walk under the raised load
- C: Start to run so that you are not under the load for very long
- D: Wait or go around, but never walk under a raised load

12.16

A mobile plant operator can let people ride in the machine:

- A: if they have a long way to go
- B: if it is raining
- C: if it is designed to carry passengers
- D: at any time

12.17

You see a mobile crane lifting a load. The load is about to hit something. What should you do?

- A: Go and tell the site manager
- B: Tell the person supervising the lift
- C: Go and tell the crane driver
- D: Do nothing and assume everything is under control

12.18

You think a load is about to fall from a moving forklift truck. What should you do?

- A: Keep clear but try to warn the driver and others in the area
- B: Run alongside the machine and try to hold on to the load
- C: Run and tell the site manager
- D: Sound the nearest fire alarm bell

12.19

The correct procedure for using a tower-crane to off-load a lorry is for:

- A: lorry drivers to sling the load before the trained slinger / signaller arrives
- B: anyone to sling the load providing it will not pass over people when on the crane
- C: a trained slinger / signaller to carry out the off-loading operation
- D: the crane driver to instruct an operative to sling the load

Answers: 12.15 = D, 12.16 = C, 12.17 = B, 12.18 = A, 12.19 = C

12.20

While visiting site you notice a build-up of diesel fumes in the area of the site that you are visiting. What is the correct course of action you should take? You should:

A: turn off the piece of plant that is creating the fumes

B: quickly inform the site manager of this hazardous situation

C: carry out the visit quickly to mimimise exposure

D: move out of the affected area at regular intervals to get fresh air

12.21

Which of the following is the most effective way of preventing pedestrians being struck by site vehicles?

A: All vehicles must switch on their flashing amber beacon

B: Separate access gates and routes for pedestrians and vehicles

C: Hi-vis vests being worn when pedestrians walk up the site road

D: A wide site road with a good quality surface

12.22

Of the following, which is the best risk control measure with regard to site vehicles reversing?

A: Setting a speed limit on site

B: Vehicles fitted with reversing bleepers

C: A signaller to reverse all vehicles especially on and off site

D: All vehicles fitted with CCTV to help them reverse

12.23

All lifting equipment must be:

A: brightly coloured, inspected and clearly signed

B: regularly maintained, clean and tidy

C: logged, inspected, tested, thoroughly examined and marked

D: strong enough for the load and always fitted with outriggers

12.24

Which of the following represents good site management on the public road approaching a site?

- A: A place where drivers can park delivery lorries off the road
- B: Items of plant parked to free-up space on site
- C: Pallets of materials stacked on the footpath
- D: Gates which swing into the road when open

12.25

When you walk across the site, what is the best way to avoid an accident with mobile plant?

- A: Keep to the pedestrian routes
- B: Ride on the plant
- C: Get the attention of the driver before you get too close
- D: Wear high visibility clothing

12.26

Which of these would you **not** expect to see if site transport is well organised?

- A: Speed limits
- B: Barriers to keep pedestrians away from mobile plant and vehicles
- C: Pedestrians and mobile plant using the same routes
- D: One-way systems

13.1

If you wear hearing protection, it will:

- [ ] A: stop you hearing all noise
- [ ] B: reduce noise to an acceptable level
- [ ] C: repair your hearing if it is damaged
- [ ] D: make you hear better

13.2

Noise over a long time can damage your hearing. Can this damage be reversed?

- [ ] A: Yes, with time
- [ ] B: Yes, if you have an operation
- [ ] C: No, the damage is permanent
- [ ] D: Yes, if you change jobs

13.3

If you need to wear hearing protection, you must remember that:

- [ ] A: you have to carry out your own noise assessment
- [ ] B: you have to pay for all hearing protection
- [ ] C: ear plugs don't work
- [ ] D: you may be less aware of what is going on around you

13.4

Two recommended ways to protect your hearing are by using:

- [ ] A: your hands to cover your ears
- [ ] B: cotton wool pads over your ears
- [ ] C: ear plugs
- [ ] D: soft cloth pads over your ears
- [ ] E: ear defenders

13.5

How can noise affect your health? Give **two** answers.

- [ ] A: Headaches
- [ ] B: Ear infections
- [ ] C: Hearing loss
- [ ] D: Waxy ears
- [ ] E: Vibration white finger

13.6

You need to wear ear defenders, but an ear pad is missing from one of the shells. What should you do?

- [ ] A: Leave them off and go onto site without any hearing protection
- [ ] B: Put them on and go onto site with them as they are
- [ ] C: Do not visit noisy areas on site until they are replaced
- [ ] D: Wrap your handkerchief around the shell and carry on with your site visit

---

Answers: 13.1 = B, 13.2 = C, 13.3 = D, 13.4 = C,E, 13.5 = A,C, 13.6 = C

13.7

Why is vibration a serious health issue?

- [ ] A: There are no early warning signs
- [ ] B: The long-term effects of vibration are not known
- [ ] C: There is no way that exposure to vibration can be prevented
- [ ] D: Vibration can cause a disabling injury that cannot be cured

13.8

What is **vibration white finger**?

- [ ] A: A mild skin rash that will go away
- [ ] B: A serious skin condition that will not clear up
- [ ] C: Severe frostbite
- [ ] D: A sign of damage to someone's hands and arms that might not go away

13.9

Which of these is **most** likely to cause vibration white finger?

- [ ] A: Electric hoist
- [ ] B: Hammer drill
- [ ] C: Hammer and chisel
- [ ] D: Battery-powered screwdriver

13.10

After standing alongside noisy equipment, you have a 'ringing' sound in your ears. What does this mean?

- [ ] A: Your hearing has been temporarily damaged
- [ ] B: You have been subjected to vibration
- [ ] C: You are about to go down with the 'flu
- [ ] D: The noise level was high but acceptable

13.11

Hand-arm vibration can cause:

- [ ] A: skin cancer
- [ ] B: skin irritation, like dermatitis
- [ ] C: blisters to hands and arms
- [ ] D: damaged blood vessels and nerves in fingers and hands

13.12

Someone near you is using noisy equipment and you have no hearing protection. What should you do?

- [ ] A: Ask them to stop what they are doing
- [ ] B: Carry on with your work because it is always noisy on site
- [ ] C: Leave the area until you have the correct PPE
- [ ] D: Speak to the operative's supervisor

Answers: 13.7 = D, 13.8 = D, 13.9 = B, 13.10 = A, 13.11 = D, 13.12 = C

13.13

You have to inspect a site near a particular construction operation that is generating a high level of noise. It is not possible to shut the operation down. Which of the following actions would you expect to be the site manager's immediate response?

- [ ] A: Arrange for a noise assessment to be carried out
- [ ] B: Make hearing protection available to those people who ask for it
- [ ] C: Issue all people affected with hearing protection as a precaution
- [ ] D: Erect 'Hearing protection zone' signs

13.14

Noise can damage your hearing. What is an early sign of this?

- [ ] A: There are no early signs
- [ ] B: Temporary deafness
- [ ] C: A skin rash around the ears
- [ ] D: Ear infections

13.15

If you have to enter a 'hearing protection zone', you must:

- [ ] A: not make any noise
- [ ] B: wear hearing protection at all times
- [ ] C: take hearing protection with you in case you need to use it
- [ ] D: wear hearing protection if the noise gets too loud for you

13.16

Noise **may** be a problem if you have to shout to be clearly heard by someone who is standing:

- [ ] A: 2 metres away
- [ ] B: 4 metres away
- [ ] C: 5 metres away
- [ ] D: 6 metres away

13.17

Operatives using machinery that can cause vibration are **less** likely to suffer from hand-arm vibration if they are:

- [ ] A: very cold but dry
- [ ] B: cold and wet
- [ ] C: warm and dry
- [ ] D: very wet but warm

Answers: 13.13 = C, 13.14 = B, 13.15 = B, 13.16 = A, 13.17 = C

14.1

What must happen each time before a shift starts work in an excavation?

- [ ] A: Someone must go in and sniff the air to see if it is safe
- [ ] B: A competent person must inspect the excavation
- [ ] C: A supervisor should stay in the excavation for the first hour
- [ ] D: A supervisor should watch from the top for the first hour

14.2

What is the **safe** way to get into a deep excavation?

- [ ] A: Climb down a ladder
- [ ] B: Use the buried services as steps
- [ ] C: Climb down the shoring
- [ ] D: Go down in an excavator bucket

14.3

You are in a deep trench and start to feel dizzy. What should you do?

- [ ] A: Get out, let your head clear and then go back in again
- [ ] B: Carry on working and hope that the feeling will go away
- [ ] C: Make sure that you and any others get out quickly
- [ ] D: Sit down in the trench and take a rest

14.4

If you need to work in a confined space, one duty of the **top man** is to:

- [ ] A: tell you how to work safely in confined spaces
- [ ] B: enter the confined space if there is a problem
- [ ] C: start the rescue plan if needed
- [ ] D: supervise the work in the confined space

14.5

Which of these is **not** a hazard in a confined space?

- [ ] A: Toxic gas
- [ ] B: A lack of carbon dioxide
- [ ] C: A lack of oxygen
- [ ] D: Flammable or explosive gas

14.6

If there is sludge at the bottom of a confined space, you should:

- [ ] A: go in and then step into the sludge to see how deep it is
- [ ] B: throw something into the sludge to see how deep it is
- [ ] C: put on a disposable face-mask before you go in
- [ ] D: have the correct respiratory protective equipment and training before you go in

Answers: 14.1 = B, 14.2 = A, 14.3 = C, 14.4 = C, 14.5 = B, 14.6 = D

14.7

Why is methane gas dangerous in confined space? Give **two** answers.

- [ ] A: It can explode
- [ ] B: It makes you hyperactive
- [ ] C: You will not be able to see because of the dense fumes
- [ ] D: It makes you dehydrated
- [ ] E: You will not have enough oxygen to breathe

14.8

You are in a confined space. If the level of oxygen drops:

- [ ] A: your hearing could be affected
- [ ] B: there is a high risk of fire or explosion
- [ ] C: you could become unconscious
- [ ] D: you might get dehydrated

14.9

You have to enter a confined space. There is no rescue team or rescue plan. What should you do?

- [ ] A: Assume that a rescue team or plan is not necessary
- [ ] B: Get someone to stand at the opening with a rope
- [ ] C: Do not enter until a rescue plan and team are in place
- [ ] D: Enter the confined space but only for short spells

14.10

You are working in a confined space when you notice the smell of bad eggs. This smell is a sign of:

- [ ] A: hydrogen sulphide
- [ ] B: oxygen
- [ ] C: methane
- [ ] D: carbon dioxide

14.11

You need to walk through sludge at the bottom of a confined space. Which of these is **not** a hazard?

- [ ] A: The release of oxygen
- [ ] B: The release of toxic gases
- [ ] C: Slips and trips
- [ ] D: The release of flammable gases

14.12

Guard-rails are placed around the top of an excavation to prevent:

- [ ] A: plant from toppling into the excavation
- [ ] B: anyone falling into the trench and being injured
- [ ] C: the sides of the trench from collapsing
- [ ] D: material from spoilt heaps falling into the excavation

14.13

You are in a confined space when the gas alarm sounds. You have no respiratory protective equipment. What should you do?

- [ ] A: Switch off the alarm
- [ ] B: Get out of the confined space quickly
- [ ] C: Carry on working but do not use electrical tools
- [ ] D: Carry on working but take plenty of breaks in the fresh air

14.14

You are standing near a deep trench. A lorry backs up to the trench and the engine is left running. What should you do?

- [ ] A: Put on ear defenders to cut out the engine noise
- [ ] B: Ignore the problem, the lorry will soon drive away
- [ ] C: Look to see if there is a toxic gas meter in the trench
- [ ] D: Get everyone out of the trench quickly

14.15

The best way to avoid the potential for someone becoming trapped in an excavation is to:

- [ ] A: eliminate the need for anyone to go into it
- [ ] B: check the contractor's method statement
- [ ] C: review the last excavation inspection record
- [ ] D: go down in a cage suspended from a crane

14.16

On well managed sites one effective method of preventing falls into excavations is to identify their location. This is best done by:

- [ ] A: always leaving a pile of soil by them
- [ ] B: showing them on the plan in the site office
- [ ] C: always stand a machine by them
- [ ] D: always placing a suitable barrier around them

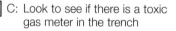

Answers: 14.13 = B, 14.14 = D, 14.15 = A, 14.16 = D

14.17

If there is the potential for work to be carried out in a confined space the **first** consideration should be whether it can be:

- [ ] A: undertaken by someone else
- [ ] B: avoided where possible
- [ ] C: managed by limiting the amount of time people are in it
- [ ] D: controlled with radios or mobile phones

14.18

An excavation must be supported if:

- [ ] A: it is more than 5 metres deep
- [ ] B: it is more than 1.2 metres deep
- [ ] C: there is a risk of the sides falling in
- [ ] D: any buried services cross the excavation

14.19

Which of these is the most accurate way to locate buried services?

- [ ] A: Cable plans
- [ ] B: Trial holes
- [ ] C: Survey drawings
- [ ] D: Architect's drawings

14.20

As part of a site survey you are required to work in a confined space. How should the air be checked?

- [ ] A: Unsafe atmospheres have a particular odour so someone should go in and smell the air
- [ ] B: No one should enter until the air has been tested with the appropriate gas detection meter
- [ ] C: Someone should look around to see if there is toxic gas
- [ ] D: Unsafe atmospheres have little oxygen so the air should be tested with a flame to see if it stays alight

14.21

You are looking at an excavation. If you see the side supports move, you should first:

- [ ] A: keep watching to see if they move again
- [ ] B: make sure that everyone working in the excavation gets out quickly
- [ ] C: do nothing as slight movement in the supports is quite normal
- [ ] D: move to another part of the excavation

Answers: 14.17 = B, 14.18 = C, 14.19 = B, 14.20 = B, 14.21 = B

14.22

Work in a confined space usually needs three **safety** documents - a risk assessment, a method statement **and:**

- [ ] A: a Permit to Work
- [ ] B: an up-to-date staff handbook
- [ ] C: a written contract for the work
- [ ] D: a company health and safety policy

14.23

You are required to undertake a survey in what you suspect might be a confined space. What should be your first consideration?

- [ ] A: Make sure that you have the correct equipment to test the atmosphere
- [ ] B: Make sure that you have a colleague with you
- [ ] C: Check if the information you need can be obtained remotely to avoid entering the space
- [ ] D: Follow a safe system of work for entering the confined space including emergency arrangements

14.24

You are arranging for an inspection in a confined space to be carried out. Which are the **two** most important safety requirements?

- [ ] A: Completing a permit to work form
- [ ] B: Informing your office before entering
- [ ] C: Entering slowly, breathing shallowly until you are sure the air is good to breathe
- [ ] D: Ensuring that a safe system of work has been identified and is followed
- [ ] E: Making sure that emergency rescue arrangements are in place

Answers: 14.22 = A, 14.23 = C, 14.24 = D,E

15.1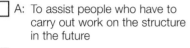

What is the purpose of the health and safety file on a construction project?

- [ ] A: To assist people who have to carry out work on the structure in the future
- [ ] B: To assist in the preparation of final accounts for the structure
- [ ] C: To record the health and safety standards of the structure
- [ ] D: To record the accident details

15.2

Which of the following is a fall-arrest system?

- [ ] A: Mobile access equipment
- [ ] B: Scaffold towers
- [ ] C: Mobile elevating work platform
- [ ] D: Safety harness and lanyard

15.3

Which piece of equipment may need to be used with a cable avoidance tool (CAT) in order to detect cables?

- [ ] A: Compressor
- [ ] B: Signal generator
- [ ] C: Battery
- [ ] D: Gas detector

15.4

In the colour coding of electrical power supplies on site, what voltage does a blue plug represent?

- [ ] A: 50 volts
- [ ] B: 110 volts
- [ ] C: 240 volts
- [ ] D: 415 volts

15.5

On the site electrical distribution system, which colour plug indicates a 415 volt supply?

- [ ] A: Yellow
- [ ] B: Blue
- [ ] C: Black
- [ ] D: Red

15.6

Which of the following is a significant hazard when excavating alongside a building or structure?

- [ ] A: Undermining the foundations of the building
- [ ] B: Upsetting the owners of the building
- [ ] C: Excavating too deep in soft ground
- [ ] D: Damage to the surface finish of the building or structure

Answers: 15.1 = A, 15.2 = D, 15.3 = B, 15.4 = C, 15.5 = D, 15.6 = A

15.7

What danger is created by excessive oxygen in a confined space?

- [ ] A: Increase in breathing rate of workers
- [ ] B: Increased flammability of combustible materials
- [ ] C: Increased working time inside work area
- [ ] D: False sense of security

15.8

What is the purpose of using a 'permit-to-work' system?

- [ ] A: To ensure that the job is being carried out properly
- [ ] B: To ensure that the job is carried out by the quickest method
- [ ] C: To enable tools and equipment to be properly checked before work starts
- [ ] D: To establish a safe system of work

15.9

An emergency route(s) must be provided on construction sites to ensure:

- [ ] A: safe passage to the ground
- [ ] B: safe passage to open air
- [ ] C: safe passage to a place of safety
- [ ] D: safe passage to the first-aid room

15.10

You are inspecting a site where there are overhead electric cables. What arrangements should a contractor normally have in place to alert those on site to the presence of the cables? Give **Two** answers.

- [ ] A: Speed ramps
- [ ] B: Warning signs
- [ ] C: Gates
- [ ] D: Barriers and goalposts
- [ ] E: Traffic lights

15.11

When is it advisable to take precautions to prevent the fall of materials into an excavation?

- [ ] A: At all times
- [ ] B: When the excavation is two or more metres deep
- [ ] C: When more than five people are working in the excavation
- [ ] D: When there is a risk from an underground cable or other service

15.12

Sole-boards may be omitted from vertical scaffold tubes if a scaffold is based on a surface of:

- [ ] A: grass
- [ ] B: sufficient strength
- [ ] C: a recently backfilled excavation
- [ ] D: firm mud

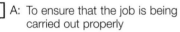

Answers: 15.7 = B, 15.8 = D, 15.9 = C, 15.10 = B,D, 15.11 = A, 15.12 = B

15.13

If a scaffold is not complete, which of the following actions should be taken by the site manager?

A: Make sure the scaffolders complete the scaffold

B: Tell all operatives not to use the scaffold

C: Use the scaffold with care and display a warning notice

D: Prevent access to the scaffold by unauthorised people

15.14

Why is it important that hazards are identified?

A: They have the potential to cause harm

B: They must all be eliminated before work can start

C: They must all be notified to the Health and Safety Executive

D: They have to be written on the Health and Safety Law poster

15.15

Under the requirements of the Work at Height Regulations, the minimum width of a working platform must be:

A: 3 scaffold boards wide

B: suitable for the job in hand

C: 2 scaffold boards wide

D: any width

15.16

If precautions are taken to prevent people and items falling, scaffold guard-rails may be temporarily removed provided that:

A: they are replaced as soon as practicable

B: the scaffolding does not become overloaded

C: the scaffolding does not begin to sway

D: the intermediate guard-rail is left in position

15.17

An assessment has been carried out under the Control of Substances Hazardous to Health Regulations. To which of the following should the risks and control measures be explained?

A: All who are working on site

B: Those on site using, or likely to be affected by, the substance

C: The person in charge of ordering materials

D: The accounts department

15.18

On a scaffold, the minimum height of the main guard-rail must be:

A: 750 mm

B: 850 mm

C: 950 mm

D: 1050 mm

Answers: 15.13 = D, 15.14 = A, 15.15 = B, 15.16 = A, 15.17 = B, 15.18 = C

15.19

When setting up a fuel storage tank on site, a spillage bund must have a minimum capacity of:

☐ A: the contents of the tank + 10%

☐ B: the contents of the tank + 15%

☐ C: the contents of the tank + 20%

☐ D: the contents of the tank + 25%

15.20

In the context of a risk assessment, what does the term 'risk' mean?

☐ A: Something with the potential to cause injury

☐ B: An unsafe act or condition

☐ C: The likelihood that harm from a particular hazard will be realised

☐ D: Any work activity that can be described as dangerous

15.21

You are inspecting an excavation into which dumpers are tipping material; what would you expect to see to prevent dumpers from falling into the excavation?

☐ A: Dumpers kept 5 metres away from the excavation

☐ B: Stop block provided parallel to the trench appropriate to the vehicle's wheel size

☐ C: Dumper drivers required to judge the distance carefully

☐ D: Dumper drivers required to approach the excavation in reverse gear

15.22

The number of people who may be carried in a passenger hoist on site must be:

☐ A: displayed in the site canteen

☐ B: displayed on a legible notice within the cage of the hoist

☐ C: given in the company safety policy

☐ D: given to the operator of the hoist

15.23

An HSE Inspector may visit a construction site:

☐ A: if 7 days' notice is given

☐ B: if any length of notice is given in writing

☐ C: at any time without notice

☐ D: only if invited by a senior member of staff

15.24

The Health and Safety at Work Act and any regulations made under that Act are:

☐ A: advisory to companies and individuals

☐ B: legally binding

☐ C: good practical advice for the employer to follow

☐ D: not compulsory, but should be complied with if convenient

Answers: 15.19 = A, 15.20 = C, 15.21 = B, 15.22 = B, 15.23 = C, 15.24 = B

15.25

The minimum level of first-aid cover required at any workplace is an appointed person. Which of the following would you expect the appointed person to carry out?

- [ ] A: Provide **most** of the care normally carried out by a first-aider
- [ ] B: Provide **all** the care normally provided by a first-aider
- [ ] C: Contact the emergency services and direct them to the scene of an accident
- [ ] D: Only apply splints to broken bones

15.26

What should the site manager do for the safety of private motorists if transport leaving site is likely to deposit mud on the public road?

- [ ] A: Have someone in the road to slow down the traffic
- [ ] B: Employ an on-site method of washing the wheels of site transport
- [ ] C: Employ a mechanical road sweeper
- [ ] D: Have someone hosing-down the mud in the road

15.27

The Beaufort Scale is important when planning any external work at height because it measures:

- [ ] A: air temperature
- [ ] B: the load-bearing capacity of a flat roof
- [ ] C: wind speed
- [ ] D: the load-bearing capacity of a scaffold

15.28

A design feature of some air bags used for fall arrest is a controlled leak rate. If these are being used, the inflation pump **must:**

- [ ] A: be electrically-powered
- [ ] B: be switched off from time to time to avoid over-inflation
- [ ] C: run all the time while work is carried out at height
- [ ] D: switched off when the air bags are full

15.29

Why is it dangerous to use inflatable air bags for fall arrest that are too big for the area to be protected?

- [ ] A: They will exert a sideways pressure on anything that is containing them
- [ ] B: The pressure in the bags will cause them to burst
- [ ] C: The inflation pump will become overloaded
- [ ] D: They will not fully inflate

15.30

Who should the contractor inform if someone reports to the site manager that they have work-related hand-arm vibration syndrome?

- [ ] A: The Health and Safety Executive
- [ ] B: The local Health Authority
- [ ] C: A coroner
- [ ] D: The nearest hospital

15.31

How should cylinders containing LPG be stored on site?

- [ ] A: In a locked cellar with clear warning signs
- [ ] B: In a locked external compound at least 3 metres from any oxygen cylinders
- [ ] C: As close to the point of use as possible
- [ ] D: Covered by a tarpaulin to shield the compressed cylinder from sunlight

15.32

How should access be controlled, if people are working in a riser shaft?

- [ ] A: By a site security operative
- [ ] B: By those who are working in it
- [ ] C: By the main contractor
- [ ] D: By a Permit to Work system

15.33

Before allowing a lifting operation to be carried out, the contractor must ensure that the sequence of operations to enable a lift to be carried out safely is confirmed in:

- [ ] A: verbal instructions
- [ ] B: a lifting plan or method statement
- [ ] C: a radio telephone message
- [ ] D: a notice in the canteen

15.34

Where should liquefied petroleum gas (LPG) cylinders be positioned when supplying an appliance in a site cabin?

- [ ] A: Inside the site cabin in a locked cupboard
- [ ] B: Under the cabin
- [ ] C: Inside the cabin next to the appliance
- [ ] D: Outside the cabin

15.35

Welding is about to start on the site you are visiting. What should be provided to prevent **passers-by** from getting arc-eye?

- [ ] A: Warning signs
- [ ] B: Screens
- [ ] C: PPE
- [ ] D: Nothing

Answers: 15.30 = A, 15.31 = B, 15.32 = D, 15.33 = B, 15.34 = D, 15.35 = B

15.36

Why may young people be more at risk of having accidents?

- A: Legislation does not apply to anyone under 18 years of age
- B: They are usually left to work alone to gain experience
- C: They are inexperienced and may not recognise danger
- D: There is no legal duty to provide them with PPE

15.37

What is the **least** reliable source of information when assessing the level of vibration from a powered percussive hand tool?

- A: In-use vibration measurement of the tool
- B: Vibration figures taken from the tool manufacturer's hand book
- C: The judgment of the site manager based upon observation
- D: Vibration data from the HSE's master list

15.38

When planning an inspection in a confined space, what should be the **first** consideration?

- A: How long the job will take
- B: To avoid the need for anyone to enter the space
- C: What people will be required
- D: Personal protective equipment

15.39

What is the best way for a responsible person to make sure that all who are doing a job have fully understood a method statement?

- A: Put the method statements in a labelled spring-binder in the office
- B: Explain the method statement to those doing the job
- C: Make sure that those doing the job have read the method statement
- D: Display the method statements on a notice board in the office

15.40

You are on site when an HSE Inspector visits. He asks to see your records for an activity that you have been monitoring. What should you do?

- A: Hand the records over
- B: Remove any pages that you feel may be incriminating before handing the records over
- C: Refuse to hand over the records due to contactural issues
- D: Refuse to hand over the records until you have consulted with your Senior Management

15.41

From a safety point of view, which of the following should be considered first when deciding on the number and location of access and egress points to a site?

- [ ] A: Parking for senior managers' cars
- [ ] B: Access for the emergency services
- [ ] C: Access for heavy vehicles
- [ ] D: Site security

15.42

Which one of the following directly controls the way works are undertaken on site?

- [ ] A: The Principal Contractor's Health and Safety Policy Statement
- [ ] B: The local Health and Safety Executive inspector
- [ ] C: The Principal Contractor's construction phase plan
- [ ] D: The Health and Safety at Work etc Act 1974

15.43

In order to manage the safety of site visitors which of the following documents must the Principal Contractor keep under review?

- [ ] A: The health and safety file
- [ ] B: Designers' risk assessments
- [ ] C: Project programme
- [ ] D: The construction phase health and safety plan

15.44

The practical way for the Principal Contractor to ensure co-operation from subcontractors is to:

- [ ] A: monitor their works, explain their legal duties and help them comply
- [ ] B: haul them over the coals when they do something wrong
- [ ] C: withhold payments when they do not perform satisfactorily
- [ ] D: wait to make comments at the next progress meeting

Answers: 15.41 = B, 15.42 = C, 15.43 = D, 15.44 = A

15.45

Having completed their risk assessment, what is the usual method used by contractors to control an ongoing, hazardous activity?

☐ A: By banning it from site

☐ B: By ensuring that the foreman always does it

☐ C: By standing over the operative whilst he does it

☐ D: By having a Permit system

15.46

On a contaminated land remediation project, which of the following would you expect to be in place to avoid contamination of the surrounding area?

☐ A: Warning signs that state that visitiors are excluded from the site

☐ B: Overalls for all visitors

☐ C: Adequate provision for vehicle wheel washing

☐ D: Respiratory protective equipment for all visitors

15.47

On a contaminated land remediation project, what should be provided to help protect the health of all who work and visit the site? Provide **two** answers.

☐ A: Lockable skips

☐ B: Plenty of fresh drinking water

☐ C: Good signage of contaminated areas

☐ D: Good welfare facilities

☐ E: Site visitors and workers log-book

15.48

On what basis would you expect the topics for toolbox talks to be selected?

☐ A: They are picked at random from the list of toolbox talks

☐ B: So that the topic relates to work that is being carried out at that time

☐ C: The client selects the topic for each talk

☐ D: In strict order so that each talk is given at least once a year

Answers: 15.45 = D, 15.46 = C, 15.47 = C,D, 15.48 = B

15.49

A planned task which involves significant risk should only be undertaken by:

A: a competent person

B: whoever can do it most quickly

C: a person who has got the time

D: Health and Safety professionals

15.50

You are aware that a particular activity is being carried out under a permit to work system. This tells you that:

A: an HSE inspector is visiting the site

B: the HSE have authorised the job to proceed

C: particular hazards have been identified for which additional control measures were necessary

D: a minimum of three people are necessary for the job to be carried out safely

15.51

Which of the following provides a good **first impression** of how well a site is currently being run?

A: How tidy it is

B: What the contractor says in the monthly site meeting

C: What last month's health and safety inspection report says

D: How often tool-box talks are given

15.52

What is the main benefit and purpose of toolbox talks?

A: They are something for the operatives to do when it is raining

B: They are a way of checking on the presence of site staff

C: They update personnel on how to approach a particular issue

D: They replace the need for induction training for operatives

15.53

The standards of health and safety on a project site have noticeably declined. As the responsible professional, what is the **first** thing you should do to find out about the Contractor's attitude to health and safety?

A: Review their health and safety inspection reports

B: Go out on site and look

C: Start a dialogue with the site manager

D: Call the Contractor's safety department

Answers: 15.49 = A, 15.50 = C, 15.51 = A, 15.52 = C, 15.53 = C

15.54

On visiting a site you notice that it is adjacent to a primary school. What is likely to be the **most effective** way of keeping children off construction sites?

- [ ] A: Put up 'Keep Out' posters
- [ ] B: Close and lock all doors and gates in the site security fencing
- [ ] C: Visits to local schools
- [ ] D: Send a flier to local households telling them to keep their children off site

15.55

Under the Construction (Design and Management) Regulations, which of the following must the Principal Contractor ensure is specifically provided before allowing any demolition work to commence?

- [ ] A: A construction phase safety plan
- [ ] B: The arrangements for demolition recorded in writing
- [ ] C: A generic risk assessment
- [ ] D: A pre-tender health and safety plan

15.56

To whom should the CDM Co-ordinator pass the health and safety file on completion of the construction project?

- [ ] A: The Association for Project Safety
- [ ] B: The Client
- [ ] C: The Health and Safety Executive
- [ ] D: The Designer

15.57

Where must you be able to find the name and address of the Client, CDM Co-ordinator and Principal Contractor?

- [ ] A: The construction phase health and safety plan
- [ ] B: The HSE Form F10 or the equivalent for the project
- [ ] C: Displayed on a project sign board near the welfare facilities
- [ ] D: The accident book

15.58

Which of the following would you **not** expect to contribute significantly to the practical management of health and safety on site?

- [ ] A: Subcontractors' risk assessments and method statements
- [ ] B: Subcontractors' certificate of Employers' Liability Insurance
- [ ] C: The principles of the Construction (Design and Management) Regulations
- [ ] D: The construction phase health and safety plan

15.59

Which one of the following would you expect subcontractors to primarily focus on to manage the risks arising from their work?

- [ ] A: The construction phase plan
- [ ] B: ConstructionSkills' publication Construction Site Safety (GE 700)
- [ ] C: Task-specific risk assessments and method statements
- [ ] D: The HSE Form 10 for the project

15.60

The monitoring of health and safety procedures can be proactive or reactive. Reactive monitoring means:

- [ ] A: workers only doing the work that they have been instructed to do
- [ ] B: investigating accidents and incidents after the event so that remedial action can be taken
- [ ] C: contractors making sure that worksheets are up to date
- [ ] D: contractors keeping a hazard book for use by all staff

15.61

The significant findings of a risk assessment reveal a risk to health or safety of site staff. What measure should always be considered first?

- [ ] A: Make sure personal protective equipment is available
- [ ] B: Adapt the work to the individual
- [ ] C: Give priority to those measures which protect the whole workforce
- [ ] D: Avoid the risk altogether if possible

15.62

The monitoring of health and safety procedures can be either proactive or reactive. Proactive monitoring means:

- [ ] A: contractors ensuring that staff always do the work that they have been instructed to do safely
- [ ] B: deciding how to prevent accidents similar to those that have already occurred
- [ ] C: looking at the work to be done, what could go wrong and how it could be done safely
- [ ] D: contractors checking that all staff read and understand all health and safety notices

15.63

In considering what measures to take to protect people against risks to their health and safety, personal protective equipment should always be regarded as:

- [ ] A: the first line of defence
- [ ] B: the only practical measure
- [ ] C: the best way to tackle the job
- [ ] D: the last resort

15.64

An employer has to prepare a written health and safety policy if:

- [ ] A: they employ 5 people or more
- [ ] B: they employ more than 3 people
- [ ] C: they employ a safety officer
- [ ] D: the work is going to last more than 30 days

15.65

If anyone has an accident at work this must be recorded. Accident records which can be viewed by anyone must:

- [ ] A: contain the injured person's name and address
- [ ] B: only be completed by a Site Manager or Supervisor
- [ ] C: comply with the requirements of the Data Protection Act
- [ ] D: only be kept in an electronic format

15.66

If a prohibition notice is issued by an inspector of the Health and Safety Executive or local authority:

- [ ] A: work can continue, provided that a risk assessment is carried out
- [ ] B: the work that is subject to the notice must cease
- [ ] C: the work can continue if extra safety precautions are taken
- [ ] D: the work in hand can be completed, but no new works started

15.67

The Management of Health and Safety at Work Regulations 1999 require risk assessments to be made:

- [ ] A: for all work activities
- [ ] B: when there is a danger of someone getting hurt
- [ ] C: when more than five people are employed
- [ ] D: where an accident has happened previously

15.68

Guidance notes accompanying regulations are:

- [ ] A: the health and safety rules as laid down by the employer
- [ ] B: a ConstructionSkills approved guide book on health and safety
- [ ] C: a set of health and safety guidelines provided by suppliers
- [ ] D: advice issued or supported by the Health and Safety Executive about complying with legislation

15.69

According to Health and Safety Executive figures, most accidents involving site transport are caused by vehicles:

- [ ] A: speeding
- [ ] B: ignoring one-way systems
- [ ] C: reversing
- [ ] D: being used by unqualified drivers

Answers: 15.66 = B, 15.67 = A, 15.68 = D, 15.69 = C

15.70

The significant findings of risk assessments must be recorded when more than a certain number of people are employed. How many?

☐ A: 3 or more

☐ B: 5 or more

☐ C: 6 or more

☐ D: 7 or more

15.71

Which **two** of the following factors must be considered by contractors when providing first-aid facilities on site?

☐ A: The cost of first-aid equipment

☐ B: The hazards and risks that are likely to occur

☐ C: The nature of the work carried out

☐ D: The difficulty in finding time to purchase the necessary equipment

☐ E: The space in the site office to store the necessary equipment

15.72

Which is **not** classified as a major injury under RIDDOR?

☐ A: Fractured finger

☐ B: Temporary loss of eyesight

☐ C: Fractured arm

☐ D: Broken wrist

15.73

What is the significance of the weekly or daily personal noise exposure limit value of 87dB set out in the Control of Noise at Work Regulations?

☐ A: All site personnel and visitors need to be warned if this noise level is being exceeded

☐ B: Hearing protection needs to be provided upon request if this level is likely to be exceeded

☐ C: The Principal Contractor must make sure everyone wears their hearing protection if this noise level is exceeded

☐ D: Employers must ensure that their personnel are not exposed to noise above this level

15.74

The Health and Safety Information for Employees Regulations require that employees be informed about specific matters of health, safety and welfare in the workplace. Under the regulations, in which **two** ways are employers allowed to communicate this information to their employees?

☐ A: By displaying the approved poster

☐ B: Verbally during site induction

☐ C: By displaying a locally produced poster

☐ D: By issuing an approved leaflet

☐ E: During a toolbox talk

Answers: 15.70 = B, 15.71 = B,C, 15.72 = A, 15.73 = D, 15.74 = A,D

15.75

Which of the following items **must** be entered on the approved Health and Safety Law poster by, or on behalf of, the employer?

- [ ] A: Details of all emergency escape routes
- [ ] B: The identity of the first-aiders
- [ ] C: The location of all fire extinguishers
- [ ] D: The address of the local Health and Safety Executive office

15.76

If an employee is injured in an accident that results in time off work, but is not a major injury, when must it be reported to the Health and Safety Executive under the Reporting of Injuries, Diseases and Dangerous Occurrences Regulations?

- [ ] A: When over half a day is lost
- [ ] B: When over 1 day is lost
- [ ] C: When over 2 days are lost
- [ ] D: When over 3 days are lost

15.77

Following the principles of prevention, which of the following is to be regarded as the **last resort** for someone's safety when working at height?

- [ ] A: Safety harness and fall arrest lanyard
- [ ] B: Mobile elevating work platform
- [ ] C: Mobile tower scaffold
- [ ] D: Access tower scaffold

15.78

Before planning for anyone to enter a confined space, following the principles of prevention, what should be the first consideration of the Contractor's responsible person?

- [ ] A: Has the atmosphere in the confined space been tested?
- [ ] B: Has a safe means of access and egress been established?
- [ ] C: Is there an alternative method of doing the work?
- [ ] D: Have all who intend to enter the confined space been properly trained?

15.79

Where a project is notifiable under the Construction (Design and Management) Regulations, what must be in place before construction work begins?

- [ ] A: Construction project health and safety file
- [ ] B: Construction phase health and safety plan
- [ ] C: Construction project plan
- [ ] D: Construction contract agreement

15.80

Where a project is notifiable under the Construction (Design and Management) Regulations, who is responsible for ensuring notification to the Health and Safety Executive of the project?

- [ ] A: Client
- [ ] B: Designer
- [ ] C: CDM Co-ordinator
- [ ] D: Principal Contractor

15.81

If a **new build** project is notifiable under the Construction (Design and Management) Regulations, the Client must ensure that construction does not start until:

- [ ] A: the construction phase health and safety plan is in place
- [ ] B: a site manager has been employed to take charge
- [ ] C: the Health and Safety Executive has given permission
- [ ] D: the health and safety file is in place

15.82

During the construction phase, the CDM Co-ordinator has responsibilities for which **two** activities under the Construction (Design and Management) Regulations?

- [ ] A: Ensuring co-operation between Designers and the Principal Contractor
- [ ] B: Appointing a competent and adequately resourced Designer
- [ ] C: Deciding which construction processes are to be used
- [ ] D: Ensuring that relevant pre-construction information is identified and collected
- [ ] E: The ongoing monitoring of site safety throughout the construction phase

15.83

Where a project is notifiable under the Construction (Design and Management) Regulations, who is responsible for preparing the construction phase health and safety plan?

- [ ] A: The Principal Contractor
- [ ] B: The Client
- [ ] C: A contractor tendering for the project
- [ ] D: The CDM Co-ordinator

15.84

Except for work being carried out for a domestic client, under the Construction (Design and Management) Regulations, in which of the following situations must the Health and Safety Executive be notified of a project?

- [ ] A: Where the work will last more than 30 days or more than 500 person-days
- [ ] B: Where the building and construction work will last more than 300 person-days
- [ ] C: Where there is more than one building to be erected
- [ ] D: When the work will take place outside normal hours

15.85

Under the Construction (Design and Management) Regulations, which of the following is responsible for **initially** making pre-construction information available?

- [ ] A: The CDM Co-ordinator
- [ ] B: The Principal Contractor
- [ ] C: The Client
- [ ] D: The Client's agent

15.86

You are required to make a site inspection in a supported excavation. The Construction (Design and Management) Regulations require a supported excavation to be inspected:

- [ ] A: every 7 days
- [ ] B: at the start of the shift when the work is to be carried out
- [ ] C: once a month
- [ ] D: when it is more than 2 metres deep

Answers: 15.83 = A, 15.84 = A, 15.85 = C, 15.86 = B

15.87

Before starting any construction work lasting more than 30 days, or 500 person-days, which of the following must be done?

- A: The local authority must be informed on a Form F9
- B: The health and safety file must be handed to the Client
- C: The Client must prepare a pre-tender health and safety plan
- D: The Health and Safety Executive must be notified

15.88

Where a project is notifiable under the requirements of the Construction (Design and Management) Regulations, what has to be displayed on a construction site?

- A: Notice of application to erect hoardings
- B: Notice of the Principal Contractor's health and safety policy
- C: Form F10 (Rev) or a notice carrying specified information
- D: A statement by the Client

15.89

If there is a fatal accident on site, when must the Health and Safety Executive be informed?

- A: Immediately
- B: Within 5 days
- C: Within 7 days
- D: Within 10 days

15.90

Following a reportable dangerous occurrence, when must the Health and Safety Executive be informed?

- A: Within 1 day
- B: Within 5 days
- C: Within 10 days
- D: Immediately

15.91

Employers must prevent exposure of their employees to substances hazardous to health, where this is reasonably practicable. If it is not reasonably practicable, which of the following should be **considered first**?

- A: What instruction, training and supervision to provide
- B: What health surveillance arrangements will be needed
- C: How to minimise risk and control exposure
- D: How to monitor the exposure of employees in the workplace

16.1

If there are any doubts as to a building's stability, a demolition contractor should consult:

- [ ] A: another demolition contractor
- [ ] B: a structural engineer
- [ ] C: an HSE Factory Inspector
- [ ] D: the company safety adviser

16.2

What should a contractor do if they discover underground services not previously identified?

- [ ] A: Fill in the hole and say nothing to anyone
- [ ] B: Stop work until the situation has been resolved
- [ ] C: Cut the pipe or cable to see if it's live
- [ ] D: Get the machine driver to dig it out

16.3

You are required to visit a demolition site. What is the most common source of high levels of lead in the atmosphere during demolition work?

- [ ] A: Stripping lead sheeting
- [ ] B: Cutting lead-covered cable
- [ ] C: Cold cutting fuel tanks
- [ ] D: Hot cutting coated steel

16.4

What type of fire extinguisher should **not** be provided where petrol is being stored?

- [ ] A: Foam
- [ ] B: Water
- [ ] C: Dry powder
- [ ] D: Carbon dioxide

16.5

What action should be taken if the contractor discovers unlabelled drums or containers on site?

- [ ] A: Put them in the nearest waste skip
- [ ] B: Ignore them. They will get flattened during the demolition
- [ ] C: Stop work until they have been safely dealt with
- [ ] D: Open them and smell the contents

16.6

Which is the safest method of demolishing brick or internal walls by hand?

- [ ] A: Undercut the wall at ground level
- [ ] B: Work across in even courses from the ceiling down
- [ ] C: Work from the doorway at full height
- [ ] D: Cut down at corners and collapse in sections

Answers: 16.1 = B, 16.2 = B, 16.3 = D, 16.4 = B, 16.5 = C, 16.6 = B

16.7

Who should be consulted before demolition is carried out near to overhead cables?

☐ A: The Health and Safety Executive

☐ B: The Fire Service

☐ C: The electricity supply company

☐ D: The land owner

16.8

Where would you find the intended method of controlling identified hazards on a demolition project?

☐ A: The structural plans

☐ B: The written arrangements for demolition

☐ C: The site welfare plans

☐ D: The Health and Safety Law poster

16.9

Before a contractor enters large open-topped tanks, what is the most important thing they should obtain?

☐ A: A ladder for easy access

☐ B: A valid permit to work

☐ C: An operative to keep watch

☐ D: A gas meter to detect any gas

16.10

After exposure to lead, what precautions should you take before eating or drinking?

☐ A: Wash your hands and face

☐ B: Do not smoke

☐ C: Change out of dirty clothes

☐ D: Rinse your mouth with clean water

16.11

What type of fire extinguisher should you **not** use in confined spaces?

☐ A: Water

☐ B: Carbon dioxide

☐ C: Dry powder

☐ D: Foam

16.12

Before carrying out the demolition cutting of fuel tanks, what should be obtained?

☐ A: A gas free certificate

☐ B: An isolation certificate

☐ C: A risk assessment

☐ D: A COSHH assessment

16.13

What do the letters SWL stand for?

- A: Satisfactory working limit
- B: Safe working level
- C: Satisfactory weight limit
- D: Safe working load

16.14

Which of the following is **true** as regards the safe working load of a piece of equipment?

- A: It must never be exceeded
- B: It is a guide figure that may be exceeded slightly
- C: It may be exceeded by 10% only
- D: It gives half the maximum weight to be lifted

16.15

What should be clearly marked on all lifting gear?

- A: Date of manufacture
- B: Name of maker
- C: Date next due for test
- D: Safe working load

16.16

What action should be taken by the contractor if a wire rope sling is defective?

- A: Do not use it and make sure that no one else can
- B: Only use it for up to half its safe working load
- C: Put it to one side to wait for repair
- D: Only use it for small lifts under 1 tonne

16.17

With regard to mobile plant, what safety feature is provided by FOPS?

- A: The speed is limited when tracking over hard surfaces
- B: The machine stops automatically if the operator lets go of the controls
- C: The operator is protected from falling materials
- D: The reach is limited when working near to live overhead cables

16.18

Which one of the following is an effective way of ensuring good standards of health and safety on a demolition project?

- A: Checking the contractor's method statement
- B: Selecting a competent demolition contractor
- C: Ensuring operatives use personal protective equipment as necessary
- D: All of the other answers

16.19

Every demolition contractor undertaking demolition operations must **first** appoint:

- A: a competent person to supervise the work
- B: a subcontractor to strip out the buildings
- C: a safety officer to check on health and safety compliance
- D: a quantity surveyor to price the extras

16.20

Which **two** of the following documents refer to the specific hazards associated with demolition work in confined spaces?

- A: A safety policy
- B: A permit-to-work
- C: A risk assessment
- D: A scaffolding permit
- E: The HSE Health and Safety Law poster

16.21

When asbestos material is suspected in buildings to be demolished, what is the **first** priority?

- A: A competent person carries out an asbestos survey
- B: Notify the HSE of the possible presence of asbestos
- C: Remove and dispose of the asbestos
- D: Employ a licensed asbestos remover

16.22

Which asbestos material, whilst requiring adequate controls, is classified as 'non-notifiable' under the Control of Asbestos Regulations?

- A: Asbestos cement
- B: Asbestos insulation / coatings
- C: Asbestos insulation board
- D: Asbestos pipe lagging

Plumbing or Gas

17.1

The legionella bacteria that cause Legionnaire's disease are most likely to be found in which of the following?

- A: A boiler operating at a temperature of 80° centigrade
- B: A shower hose outlet
- C: A cold water storage cistern containing water at 10° centigrade
- D: A WC toilet pan

17.2

How are legionella bacteria passed on to humans?

- A: Through fine water droplets such as sprays or mists
- B: By drinking dirty water
- C: Through contact with the skin
- D: From other people when they sneeze

17.3

The reason for carrying out temporary continuity bonding before removing and replacing sections of metallic pipework is to:

- A: provide a continuous earth for the pipework installation
- B: prevent any chance of blowing a fuse
- C: maintain the live supply to the electrical circuit
- D: prevent any chance of corrosion to the pipework

17.4

Apart from the cylinders used in gas-powered forklift trucks, you should never see liquefied petroleum gas cylinders placed on their sides during use because:

- A: it would give a faulty reading on the contents gauge, resulting in flashback
- B: air could be drawn into the cylinder, creating a dangerous mixture of gases
- C: the liquid gas would be at too low a level to allow the torch to burn correctly
- D: the liquid gas could be drawn from the cylinder, creating a safety hazard

17.5

What is the preferred method of checking for leaks when assembling liquefied petroleum gas equipment before use?

- A: Test with a lighted match
- B: Sniff the connections to detect the smell of gas
- C: Listen to hear for escaping gas
- D: Apply leak detection fluid to the connections

Answers: 17.1 = B, 17.2 = A, 17.3 = A, 17.4 = D, 17.5 = D

17.6

What is the colour of propane gas cylinders?

☐ A: Black

☐ B: Maroon

☐ C: Red / Orange

☐ D: Blue

17.7

You arrive to carry out a site inspection that involves using ladder access to a roof. You notice the ladder has been painted. You should:

☐ A: only use the ladder if it is made of metal

☐ B: only use the ladder if it is made of wood

☐ C: only use the ladder if wearing rubber-soled boots to prevent slipping

☐ D: not use the ladder, and report the matter to the site manager

17.8

Which of the following makes it essential for contractors to take great care when handling oxygen cylinders?

☐ A: They contain highly flammable compressed gas

☐ B: They contain highly flammable liquid gas

☐ C: They are filled to extremely high pressures

☐ D: They contain poisonous gas

17.9

What is the colour of an acetylene cylinder?

☐ A: Orange

☐ B: Black

☐ C: Green

☐ D: Maroon

17.10

Which of the following is the safest place for contractors to store oxyacetylene gas welding bottles when they are not in use?

☐ A: Outside in a special storage compound

☐ B: In company vehicles

☐ C: Inside the building in a locked cupboard

☐ D: In the immediate work area, ready for use the next day

17.11

Which of the following **is most likely** to result in those who work with sheet lead having raised levels of lead in their blood?

☐ A: By them not using the correct respirator

☐ B: By not washing their hands before eating

☐ C: By not changing out of their work clothes

☐ D: By them not wearing safety goggles

17.12

What item of personal protective equipment, from the following list, should be used when someone is oxyacetylene welding?

- [ ] A: Ear defenders
- [ ] B: Clear goggles
- [ ] C: Green-tinted goggles
- [ ] D: Dust mask

17.13

When observing oxyacetylene welding equipment being used on site, the bottles should be:

- [ ] A: laid on their side
- [ ] B: stood upright
- [ ] C: stood upside down
- [ ] D: angled at 45°

17.14

When working in an area where fibreglass roof insulation is being handled, in addition to safety boots and helmet, which of the following items of personal protective equipment (PPE) should be worn?

- [ ] A: Gloves, face mask and eye protection
- [ ] B: Rubber apron, eye protection and ear defenders
- [ ] C: Ear defenders, face mask and boots
- [ ] D: Barrier cream, eye protection and face mask

Answers: 17.12 = C, 17.13 = B, 17.14 = A

18.1

What are **two** effects of under-inflated tyres on the operation of a machine?

- [ ] A: It decreases the operating speed of the engine
- [ ] B: It leads to instability of the machine
- [ ] C: It causes increased tyre wear
- [ ] D: It decreases tyre wear
- [ ] E: It increases the operating speed of the engine

18.2

Which of the following is **true** as regards the safe working load of lifting equipment such as a cherry picker, lorry loader or excavator?

- [ ] A: It must never be exceeded
- [ ] B: It is a guide figure that may be exceeded slightly
- [ ] C: It may be exceeded by 10% only
- [ ] D: It gives half the maximum weight to be lifted

18.3

Which of the following checks should the operator of a mobile elevating work platform, for example a cherry picker, carry out before using it?

- [ ] A: Check that a seat belt is provided for the operator
- [ ] B: Check that a roll-over cage is fitted
- [ ] C: Drain the hydraulic system
- [ ] D: Check that emergency systems operate correctly

18.4

In which of the following circumstances would it **not** be safe to use a cherry picker for working at height?

- [ ] A: When a roll-over cage is not fitted
- [ ] B: When the ground is uneven and sloping
- [ ] C: When weather protection is not fitted
- [ ] D: When the operator is clipped to an anchorage point in the basket

18.5

When providing portable traffic signals on minor rural roads used by cyclists and horse riders, what action should be taken by the contractor?

- [ ] A: Locate the signals at bends in the road
- [ ] B: Allow more time for slow-moving traffic by increasing the 'all red' phase of the signals
- [ ] C: Operate the signals manually
- [ ] D: Use 'stop/go' boards only

18.6

What is the purpose of an on-site risk assessment?

- [ ] A: To ensure there is no risk of traffic build-up due to the works in progress
- [ ] B: To review the hazards and risks to ensure that the planned safety system is still applicable
- [ ] C: To ensure that the work can be carried out in a reasonable timeframe
- [ ] D: To protect the employer from prosecution

18.7

When undertaking a site survey on a dual carriageway with a 60 mph speed limit, what is the **minimum** standard of high-visibility clothing which must be worn?

- [ ] A: Reflective waistcoat
- [ ] B: Reflective long-sleeved jacket
- [ ] C: None
- [ ] D: Reflective sash

18.8

Why should temporary signing be removed when works are complete?

- [ ] A: To get traffic flowing
- [ ] B: It is a legal requirement
- [ ] C: To allow the road to be opened fully
- [ ] D: To reuse signs on new job

18.9

When should installed signs and guarding equipment be inspected?

- [ ] A: After it has been used
- [ ] B: Once a week
- [ ] C: Before being used
- [ ] D: Regularly and at least once every day

Answers: 18.5 = B, 18.6 = B, 18.7 = B, 18.8 = B, 18.9 = D

18.10

What **two** site conditions must prevail so that the minimum traffic management can be used?

- [ ] A: Traffic should be heavy
- [ ] B: Visibility is good
- [ ] C: Double parking will be required
- [ ] D: Rush hour
- [ ] E: Period of low risk

18.11

What traffic management is required when carrying out a maintenance job on a motorway?

- [ ] A: The same as would be required on a single carriageway
- [ ] B: A flashing beacon and a 'keep left/right' sign
- [ ] C: A scheme installed by a registered traffic management contractor
- [ ] D: Ten 1-metre high cones and a 1-metre high 'men working' sign

18.12

What is the minimum traffic management required when carrying out a short term minor maintenance job in a quiet, low-speed side road?

- [ ] A: A flashing amber beacon and a 'keep left/right' arrow
- [ ] B: The same as required for a road excavation
- [ ] C: Five cones and a blue arrow
- [ ] D: Temporary traffic lights

18.13

Mobile works are being carried out by day. A single vehicle is being used. What must be conspicuously displayed on or at the rear of the vehicle?

- [ ] A: Road narrows (left or right)
- [ ] B: A specific task warning sign (for example, gully cleaning)
- [ ] C: A 'keep left/right' arrow
- [ ] D: A 'roadworks ahead' sign

18.14

What action is required when a vehicle fitted with a direction arrow is travelling from site to site?

- [ ] A: Point the direction arrow up
- [ ] B: Travel slowly from site to site
- [ ] C: Point the direction arrow down
- [ ] D: Cover or remove the direction arrow

18.15

Signs placed on footways must be located so that they:

- [ ] A: block the footway
- [ ] B: can be read by site personnel
- [ ] C: do not create a hazard for pedestrians
- [ ] D: can be easily removed

18.16

When drivers who are approaching roadworks cannot easily see any advance roadwork signs because of poor visibility or other obstructions, the contractor should:

- [ ] A: place additional signs in advance of the works
- [ ] B: extend the safety zones
- [ ] C: extend the sideways clearance
- [ ] D: lengthen the lead-in taper

18.17

What action is required where passing traffic may block the view of signs?

- [ ] A: Signs must be larger
- [ ] B: Signs must be duplicated on both sides of the road
- [ ] C: Signs must be placed higher
- [ ] D: Additional signs must be placed in advance of the works

18.18

In which **two** places would you find information on the distances for setting out the signs in advance of the works under different road conditions?

- [ ] A: In the Traffic Signs Manual (Chapter 8)
- [ ] B: In the 'Pink Book'
- [ ] C: On the back of the sign
- [ ] D: In the specification for highway works
- [ ] E: The Code of Practice ('Red Book')

18.19

Signs, lights and guarding equipment must be properly secured:

- [ ] A: with sacks containing fine granular material set at a low level
- [ ] B: by roping them to concrete blocks or kerb stones
- [ ] C: to prevent them being stolen
- [ ] D: by iron weights suspended from the frame by chains or other strong material

Answers: 18.15 = C, 18.16 = A, 18.17 = B, 18.18 = A,E, 18.19 = A

18.20

Which is **not** an approved means of controlling traffic at roadworks?

☐ A: Priority signs

☐ B: Police supervision

☐ C: Hand signals by operatives

☐ D: A give-and-take system

18.21

What action is required where it is **not** possible to maintain the correct safety zone?

☐ A: Barrier off the working space

☐ B: Place additional advance signing

☐ C: Use extra cones on the lead-in taper

☐ D: Stop work and review arrangements

18.22

What is the purpose of the 'safety zone'?

☐ A: To indicate the works area

☐ B: To protect you from the traffic and the traffic from you

☐ C: To allow extra working space in an emergency

☐ D: To give a safe route around the working area

18.23

When should you switch on the amber flashing beacon fitted to your vehicle?

☐ A: At all times

☐ B: When travelling to and from the depot

☐ C: When the vehicle is being used as a works vehicle

☐ D: Only in poor visibility

18.24

When driving into a site works access on a motorway, what must you do approximately 200 metres before the access?

☐ A: Switch on the vehicle hazard lights

☐ B: Switch on the flashing amber beacon

☐ C: Switch on the headlights

☐ D: Switch on the flashing amber beacon and the appropriate indicator

18.25

Lifting equipment for carrying persons, for example a cherry picker, must be thoroughly examined by a competent person every:

☐ A: 12 months

☐ B: 24 months

☐ C: 18 months

☐ D: 6 months

Answers: 18.20 = C, 18.21 = D, 18.22 = B, 18.23 = C, 18.24 = D, 18.25 = D

18.26

From a safety point of view, diesel must not be used to prevent asphalt sticking to the bed of lorries because:

- [ ] A: it will create a slipping hazard
- [ ] B: it will corrode the bed of the lorry
- [ ] C: it will create a fire hazard
- [ ] D: it will react with the asphalt, creating explosive fumes

18.27

When kerbing works are being carried out, which method should be used for getting kerbs off the vehicle?

- [ ] A: Lift them off manually using the correct technique
- [ ] B: Push them off the back
- [ ] C: Use mechanical means, such as a JCB fitted with a grab
- [ ] D: Ask your workmate to give you a hand

18.28

Why is it necessary to wear high-visibility clothing when working on roads?

- [ ] A: So road users and plant operators can see you
- [ ] B: So that your colleagues can see you
- [ ] C: Because you were told to
- [ ] D: Because it will keep you warm

18.29

In which of the following circumstances can someone enter the safety zone?

- [ ] A: To store unused plant
- [ ] B: To maintain cones and signs
- [ ] C: To park site vehicles
- [ ] D: To store materials

18.30

If you are working after dark, is mobile plant exempt from the requirement to show lights?

- [ ] A: Yes, on all occasions
- [ ] B: Yes if authorised by the site manager
- [ ] C: Only if they are not fitted to the machine as standard
- [ ] D: Not in any circumstances

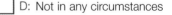
Answers: 18.26 = A, 18.27 = C, 18.28 = A, 18.29 = B, 18.30 = D

ConstructionSkills wishes to acknowledge the assistance offered by the following organisations in the development of health and safety testing:

Health and Safety Test Question Sub-Committee

ConstructionSkills (NI)

Construction Employers Federation Limited (CEF NI)

Driving Standards Agency

Heating and Ventilating Contractors' Association (HVCA)

Highways Agency

Joint Industry Board – Plumbing, Mechanical and Electrical Services

Lift and Escalator Industry Association (LEIA)

Management Board of the Construction Skills Certification Scheme

National Demolition Training Group

Scottish and Northern Ireland Joint Industry Board for the Plumbing Industry

Notes

Notes

Notes

Notes

Notes

Notes

Notes